Workout

Skills Review & Practice

Reading Grade 4

W9-AYG-157

Triumph Learning®

Workout, Reading Grade 4
263NA
ISBN-10: 1-60471-114-0
ISBN-13: 978-1-60471-114-1

Cover Image: © Ralph Voltz/Deborah Wolfe Ltd.; © iStockphoto/John Rodriguez;
© Rubberball/Jupiterimages; © Rubberball/Photolibrary; © Photoalto/Photolibrary;
© Photodisc/Photolibrary.

Triumph Learning® 136 Madison Avenue, 7th Floor, New York, NY 10016
Kevin McAliley, President and Chief Executive Officer

© 2009 Triumph Learning, LLC

All rights reserved. No part of this publication may be reproduced in whole or in part, stored
in a retrieval system, or transmitted in any form or by any means, electronic, mechanical,
photocopying, recording or otherwise, without written permission from the publisher.

Printed in the United States of America.

10 9 8

Dear Student,

Are you a reading champion?

You will be when you use

Workout!

Getting in shape is easy.

Just complete the lessons inside.

So, on your mark, get set – Work Out!

This book belongs to _____

Table of Contents

Unit 1: Reading for Information

Unit 2: Reading Literature

Unit 3: Writing and Editing

LESSON 1

Features of Nonfiction Texts

WORDS TO KNOW   **Heading**   a word or phrase at the top of a paragraph that tells what the paragraph is about

Review It!

Read the heading and the paragraph. Use the Hint to understand how headings help readers.

After-School Classes

Are you looking for something to do after school? Then come to the community center. There are classes for everyone—art, dance, jazz, chess, and many more!

> **Hint**   Text that looks different than the rest of the page gives special information. It tells what different parts of the text are mostly about. Notice the text in dark print.

Try It!

Read these sections from the community center catalog. As you read, underline the key words in each paragraph that tell more about the heading.

1. ### Fitness and Sports
   Keep fit! There are classes for parents and babies. Sports for kids meet after school. Special half-hour stretch classes for seniors meet twice a day.

2. ### Arts and Crafts
   Get your hands dirty in Clay Class. Learn to draw. Learn to paint. Knit a scarf. Weave a shawl. There are classes for all ages.

3. ### Music and Dance
   Let the music move you! Learn about jazz, country, and rock music. Play an instrument! Try ballet, tap, or ballroom dancing. Kids' classes meet after school. Adult classes meet after 6:00 P.M.

4. ### Story Hour
   Come and listen to wonderful storytellers. Then learn to tell stories of your own. What tales can you dream up?

Now, use the passage to answer the questions on the following page.

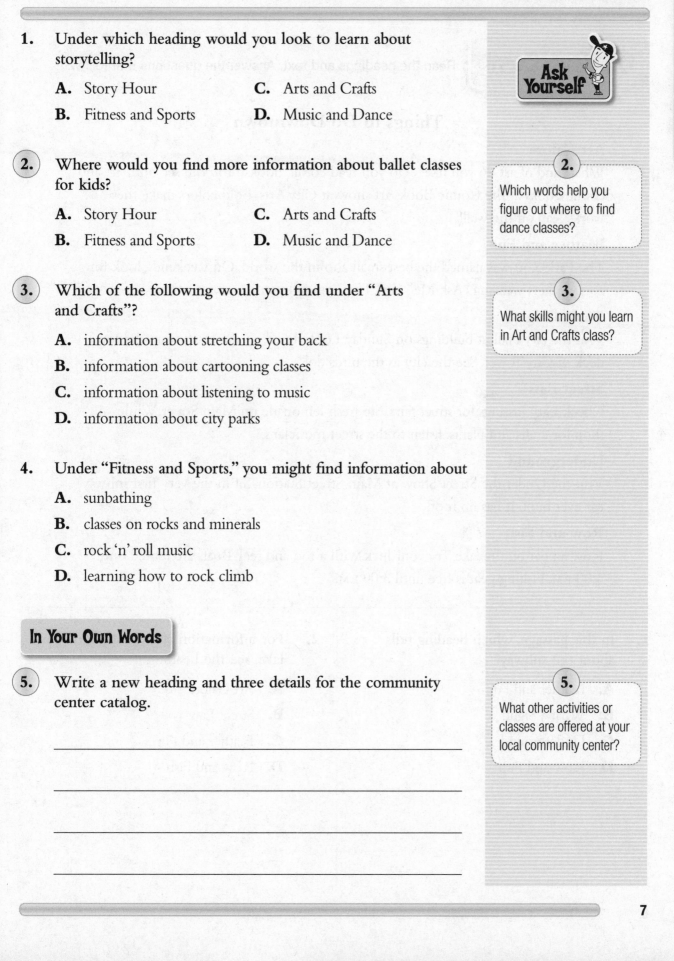

1. Under which heading would you look to learn about storytelling?

   A. Story Hour   **C.** Arts and Crafts

   B. Fitness and Sports   **D.** Music and Dance

2. Where would you find more information about ballet classes for kids?

   A. Story Hour   **C.** Arts and Crafts

   B. Fitness and Sports   **D.** Music and Dance

Ask Yourself

2. Which words help you figure out where to find dance classes?

3. Which of the following would you find under "Arts and Crafts"?

   A. information about stretching your back

   B. information about cartooning classes

   C. information about listening to music

   D. information about city parks

3. What skills might you learn in Art and Crafts class?

4. Under "Fitness and Sports," you might find information about

   A. sunbathing

   B. classes on rocks and minerals

   C. rock 'n' roll music

   D. learning how to rock climb

In Your Own Words

5. Write a new heading and three details for the community center catalog.

   _____

   _____

   _____

   _____

5. What other activities or classes are offered at your local community center?

On Your Own!

Read the headings and text. Answer the questions that follow.

Things to Do Downtown

Art Galore

What kind of art do you like? Do you read comic books? You can see both art and comic books at the Comic Book Art show at City Arts. Bold colors make these works leap off the wall!

Feather and Fur

The Park Zoo was named the best small zoo in the world. On weekends, look for zoo workers wearing "Ask Me" pins. They can tell you about the animals.

What a Sight!

Visit the city's tallest buildings on Sunday. Look down on the town from the top deck of City Tower. See the city as the birds do!

Street Eats

Check City Listings for street fairs. Sip fresh lemonade on Main Street. While you shop for crafts and plants, listen to the street musicians.

Underground

Visit the Under the Street Show at Main Street Station. Sit in the very first subway car ever built. It has no roof!

Row and Fish

Row a boat on the lake. Try your luck with a rod and reel. Boats are rented until 5:00 P.M. Fishing gear is free until 3:00 P.M.

---

1. In this passage, which heading tells about the subway?

   A. Feather and Fur

   B. What a Sight!

   C. Underground

   D. Row and Fish

2. For information about fishing on the lake, see the heading

   A. Art Galore

   B. Street Eats

   C. Feather and Fur

   D. Row and Fish

3. You might find information about monkeys under the heading

   A. Underground
   B. Street Eats
   C. Feather and Fur
   D. Art Galore

4. On a sunny day, which heading might you skip?

   A. Row and Fish
   B. Underground
   C. What a Sight!
   D. Street Eats

5. If you are afraid of heights, you might skip

   A. What a Sight!
   B. Underground
   C. Row and Fish
   D. Art Galore

6. For exercise, you could find information under the heading

   A. Row and Fish
   B. What a Sight!
   C. Underground
   D. Street Eats

Write It Out   List the headings in the correct columns on the chart.

7.

Animals	Food	Outdoors	Indoors	Views

LESSON 2 — Using Reference Sources

WORDS TO KNOW **Reference sources** books and periodicals, such as newspapers and magazines, that provide facts and information. Parts within reference sources, such as indexes and tables of contents, make finding information easier.

Review It! Read the index. Use the Hint to find out where you would find information about paper Recycling.

Recycling
   aluminum, 23
   glass, 25, 26
   paper, 27
   plastic, 28, 39

Hint Look at all the entries listed after Recycling. These are listed in alphabetical order.

Try It! Read the following index from a book about dog behavior and training. As you read, circle the main subjects included in the index.

(1) *Behavior and Training, 2–21*
(2)   *agility*
(3)   *classes, 2, 3*
(4)   *competitions, 4*
(5)   *behavior*
(6)   *correcting of inappropriate, 9*
(7)   *problems, 7, 8*
(8)   *psychology, 5, 6*
(9)   *obedience*
(10)   *classes, 10, 11*

    expectations, 10
    puppy training, 12, 13
  sports and recreation
    flyball racing, 20
    hiking, 15
    running, 18, 19
    sled dogs, 16, 17
  tracking
    scent, 21

Now, use the index to answer the questions on the following page.

1. What is the first page on which you would find information about agility?

    A. 2   **C.** 4

    B. 3   **D.** 5

2. How many pages are there about obedience?

    A. 2

    B. 3

    C. 4

    D. 5

2.
How many entries are there for *obedience*?

3. The subject that has only one page is

    A. agility

    B. behavior

    C. obedience

    D. tracking

3.
Should you count the same page number twice?

4. Which subject can be found on page 20?

    A. hiking

    B. sled dogs

    C. flyball racing

    D. running

In Your Own Words

5. Based on the index, write a title and a short sentence to describe this book.

    _____

    _____

    _____

    _____

5.
What are most of the entries about?

On Your Own!

Read this table of contents. Answer the questions that follow it.

1. The part that has the fewest chapters is

    A. Muffins

    B. Tarts

    C. Pies

    D. Crisps

2. The section of the book on crisps has

    A. 1 chapter

    B. 2 chapters

    C. 3 chapters

    D. 4 chapters

3. How many chapters contain recipes using peaches?

    A. 1

    B. 2

    C. 3

    D. 4

4. If you wanted to find a recipe for cherry tarts, you would go to page

    A. 10

    B. 14

    C. 18

    D. 22

5. On which pages would you find recipes for tarts?

    A. 16–32

    B. 14–18

    C. 55–69

    D. 34–53

6. What would be a good title for this book, based on the table of contents?

    A. Fruits Are Healthy

    B. Cooking with Fruit

    C. All About Apples

    D. I Love Peaches

Write It Out   What is another chapter you might find in this book's table of contents? Explain.

7. _____

    _____

    _____

    _____

    _____

    _____

    _____

    _____

    _____

Understanding Graphics

WORDS TO KNOW

Graphics visual aids that provide information in a clear, short form. Charts, tables, and bar graphs are examples of graphics. Bar graphs use bars instead of words to compare information.

Review It! Read the bar graph. Use the Hint to compare information about students' favorite fruits.

Favorite Fruits

> **Hint** Find the fruit name first. Then check to see the number the bar reaches.

Try It! Read the following table. As you read, <u>circle</u> the three types of information included in the table.

State	State Bird	Tree
Georgia	brown thrasher	live oak
New York	bluebird	sugar maple
Pennsylvania	ruffed grouse	eastern hemlock
Texas	mockingbird	pecan

Now, use the table to answer the questions on the following page.

1. Which state is listed first in the table?

   A. Georgia   **C.** Pennsylvania

   B. New York   **D.** Texas

Ask Yourself

2. Which two state's official birds have colors in their name?

   A. New York and Pennsylvania

   B. Georgia and Texas

   C. Georgia and New York

   D. Texas and Pennsylvania

> **2.**
> What are the names of the state birds?

3. The state tree of Texas is

   A. the sugar maple

   B. the pecan

   C. the eastern hemlock

   D. the live oak

> **3.**
> Did you look in the row for Texas and the column for tree?

4. What is the state bird of Pennsylvania?

   A. brown thrasher

   B. mockingbird

   C. bluebird

   D. ruffed grouse

In Your Own Words

5. Use information from the table. Write two sentences about state birds and trees.

   _____

   _____

   _____

   _____

> **5.**
> What information did you learn from reading the table?

On Your Own!

Read this chart about the planets in the solar system. Answer the questions that follow.

Planet	Position of Planet from the Sun	Fun Fact
Mercury	1	On the planet Mercury, there are fewer than 2 Earth days in a year.
Venus	2	Venus is the brightest planet in the sky.
Earth	3	Earth's crust is about 5 miles deep.
Mars	4	Mars is home to the largest volcano found in the solar system.
Jupiter	5	A day on the planet Jupiter lasts only 9 hours and 55 minutes.
Saturn	6	If there were a bathtub big enough to hold it, Saturn would float in the water.
Uranus	7	Uranus has been visited by only one spacecraft.
Neptune	8	One year on Neptune lasts 165 Earth years.

1. How many planets are there?

   A. 8

   B. 9

   C. 6

   D. 7

2. This chart shows how far each planet is away from the

   A. moon

   B. Earth

   C. sun

   D. Milky Way

3. Which planet has a crust about 5 miles deep?

   A. Mars

   B. Venus

   C. Jupiter

   D. Earth

4. How many planets from the sun is Uranus?

   A. 4   B. 5

   C. 6   D. 7

5. Which of the following is a fun fact about Venus?

   A. It is now called a "dwarf planet."

   B. It is the brightest planet in the sky.

   C. It has been visited by only one spacecraft.

   D. One day lasts only 9 hours and 55 minutes.

6. Which planet's fun fact is about a bathtub?

   A. Mercury   B. Pluto

   C. Saturn   D. Venus

Write It Out   Choose one planet and its fun fact from the chart. Explain why it is your favorite.

7. _____

_____

_____

_____

_____

_____

_____

_____

_____

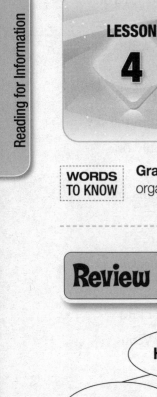

LESSON 4

Graphic Organizers

WORDS TO KNOW **Graphic organizers** illustrations that make ideas clear with lines and shapes. Graphic organizers include webs and diagrams.

Review It! Read the graphic organizer. Use the Hint to find out more information about Helen Keller.

Helen Keller

born in 1880

could not see or hear

learned to talk with her hands

Hint Be sure to read the information in each of the ovals.

Try It! Read the following graphic organizer. As you read, <u>underline</u> three interesting facts about the Grand Canyon.

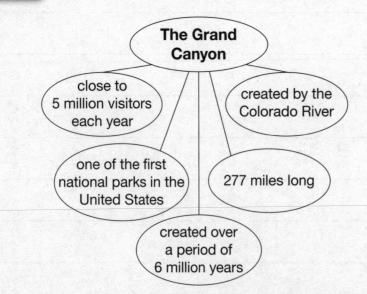

The Grand Canyon

close to 5 million visitors each year

created by the Colorado River

one of the first national parks in the United States

277 miles long

created over a period of 6 million years

Now, use the graphic organizer to answer the questions on the following page.

1. How many facts are listed in the graphic organizer?

   A. 3   **C.** 5

   B. 4   **D.** 6

2. In which country is the Grand Canyon located?

   A. Colorado

   B. Mexico

   C. Arizona

   D. United States

Ask Yourself

2.
Can you find two country names and then decide which one is correct?

3. How long is the Grand Canyon?

   A. 277 miles

   B. 5 million miles

   C. 6 million miles

   D. 377 miles

3.
In which oval did you find the answer to the question?

4. How many visitors does the Grand Canyon receive each year?

   A. about 6 million

   B. close to 5 million

   C. over 5 million

   D. less than 4 million

In Your Own Words

5. Based on the graphic organizer, write two sentences that include facts about the Grand Canyon.

   _____

   _____

   _____

   _____

5.
What information did you learn from reading the graphic organizer?

On Your Own!

Read this graphic organizer. Answer the questions that follow it.

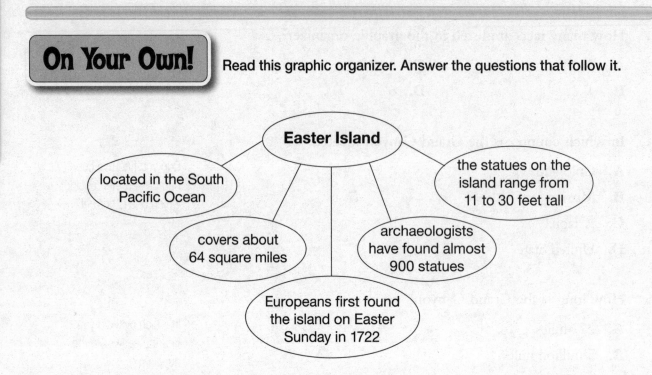

1. This graphic organizer provides information about

   A. Easter Sunday

   B. South Pacific Island

   C. North Pacific Ocean

   D. Easter Island

2. When did Europeans first find the island?

   A. 1722

   B. 1764

   C. 1700

   D. 1719

3. **Who found the statues on the island?**

   A. tourists

   B. explorers

   C. archaeologists

   D. South Pacific Islanders

4. **About how many statues have been found on Easter Island?**

   A. 64

   B. 900

   C. 1722

   D. 11 to 30

5. **An interesting fact about Easter Island is**

   A. it is located in the Atlantic Ocean

   B. it covers about 64 square miles

   C. it was discovered in 1776

   D. Americans first found the island on Easter Sunday

6. **According to the graphic organizer, the statues on the island**

   A. are not very tall

   B. were carved by Europeans

   C. are 11 to 30 feet tall

   D. are no longer standing

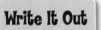 Use the information in the graphic organizer to help you write a brief answer to the question below.

7. What would you find interesting about visiting Easter Island today?

_____

_____

_____

_____

_____

_____

_____

Context Clues

WORDS TO KNOW **Context clues**   words, phrases, or sentences around or near an unfamiliar word that help you understand its meaning

Read these sentences. Use the Hint to help you figure out the unfamiliar word.

Manuel worked hard to help his brother put the boxes in the car. He had just graduated from high school. Now he was leaving to go away to college. Manuel would miss his brother, but he would also get his own room now.

> **Hint**   Here, the word *leaving* and the phrase *go away to college* help you to understand what the word *graduated* means.

Read this passage. As you read, <u>underline</u> unfamiliar words and circle context clues that help you understand each word meaning.

1   Last summer, I went to visit my grandma and grandpa. My parents drove me to their
2   house, which took about 3 hours. My grandma baked cookies and pies for me. My
3   grandpa planned a fun outing for us. He took me to the train museum. I learned about
4   the history of the **locomotive** train. The first was made in 1804. Most locomotives
5   were for **commercial** use. They didn't start to carry passengers until about 1825.
6   A **tourist** could travel over 9 miles in one hour. On the train, I saw a model of an
7   **engineer** in his uniform. I always thought an engineer is a person who helps design
8   and build bridges and roads. At the museum, I learned that an engineer is also a person
9   who drives a train.

Now, use the passage to answer the questions on the following page.

1. In line 4, *locomotive* is another word for

   A. passenger   **C.** museum

   B. moving   **D.** history

2. What does *commercial* mean in line 5?

   A. business

   B. entertainment

   C. television

   D. people

3. In line 5, the word *tourist* means

   A. a person who drives a train

   B. a person who builds bridges

   C. a person who drives a car

   D. a person who travels for pleasure

4. As used in lines 6–9, how many definitions does the word *engineer* have?

   A. 2

   B. 3

   C. 4

   D. 5

In Your Own Words

5. Rewrite the sentence on lines 7 and 8 in your own words.

_____

_____

_____

_____

Ask Yourself

2. Which sentence near the word *commercial* in line 5 helps you figure out its meaning?

3. If you replace *tourist* with each of the answer choices, which makes the most sense?

5. What do the words *design* and *build* mean in the sentence?

On Your Own!

Read this passage. Answer the questions that follow it.

I love to cook with my dad. He is a chef at a restaurant in town. It took some time to become **accustomed** to his cooking. He likes to add a lot of spices. I am used to it now. It's delicious! Dad says I have a very healthy **appetite**. He says I can eat more than he can!

One of my favorite things to cook is a **casserole**. Everything gets put into one dish and then you bake it. Some of the **ingredients** I like to use are chicken, vegetables, rice, and cheese. Sometimes I **garnish** the top with some nice green **parsley**. It makes the dish look and taste great.

Dad taught me how to make chicken and **dumplings**. The dumplings are pretty easy to make. They look like little pillows. They are made of dough and cooked in boiling oil. Dad has to do that part. Sometimes we cook them in **broth** instead. Chicken broth can be made from boiling chicken in water for many hours. It is like chicken-flavored water!

The spices I like to use most when I cook are salt and pepper. Dad uses other spices such as **paprika** for its red color and basil for its sweet **scent**. It smells fantastic!

1. In this passage, what does the word *appetite* mean?

    A. diet

    B. desire for food

    C. starvation

    D. dinner

2. The word *broth* means

    A. a chicken

    B. a dessert

    C. a dish made from dough

    D. a clear soup

3. Read this sentence from the passage.

> Some of the ingredients I like to use are chicken, vegetables, rice, and cheese.

What does the word *ingredients* mean?

- **A.** types of drinks
- **B.** parts of a chicken
- **C.** parts of a recipe
- **D.** types of vegetables

4. The word *accustomed* means

- **A.** got used to
- **B.** disliked
- **C.** tasted
- **D.** turned away

5. As used in the passage, *garnish* means to

- **A.** cook
- **B.** stir
- **C.** decorate
- **D.** bake

6. Which phrase or sentence helps you figure out the meaning of *scent*?

- **A.** other spices such as
- **B.** It smells fantastic!
- **C.** for its red color
- **D.** I like to use most

Write It Out Write the meaning for each word from the passage in the space provided in the chart.

7.

Word	Meaning
casserole	
parsley	
dumplings	
paprika	

LESSON 6 — Asking Questions

WORDS TO KNOW **Questions** can help you better understand what you're reading. Try questions beginning with *who*, *what*, *when*, *where*, *why*, and *how* first.

Review It! Read these sentences. Use the Hint to ask yourself some questions as you read.

Kyle was excited about the first day of camp. He wondered if he would go swimming right away! As the car pulled into the driveway, Kyle could hardly wait to get out.

Hint *Where* is Kyle? *What* is he thinking? *When* does the passage happen? Answering these questions will help you know what the passage is about.

Try It! Read the following passage. <u>Write</u> in the margin *who*, *what*, *when*, *where*, *why*, and *how* questions that you have.

1. Tamika slowly walked into the doctor's office with her mother. The symptoms she
2. had were a cough, a runny nose, and a fever. When it was her turn to see the doctor,
3. Tamika was a little nervous. She wasn't sure what he would tell her. She walked into
4. the room with her mother. The doctor asked Tamika to describe how she was feeling.
5. Then he asked Tamika to get up on the table so he could listen to her heart and lungs.
6. At the end of the appointment, the doctor told Tamika that she had a virus. He told
7. her mother to make sure Tamika drank a lot of fluids and got a lot of rest. He also said
8. that Tamika would start to feel better in a few days. Tamika was relieved to know that
9. she would be feeling better soon.

Now, use the passage to answer the questions on the following page.

1. Who went to the doctor's office with Tamika?

   A. her mother

   B. her father

   C. her brother

   D. her sister

Ask Yourself

1.
Who is the other person mentioned in the passage?

2. How did Tamika walk into the doctor's office?

   A. quickly   **C.** excitedly

   B. slowly   **D.** sadly

3. Why was Tamika nervous to see the doctor?

   A. She didn't like the doctor.

   B. She wanted to go home.

   C. She thought the doctor was mean.

   D. She wasn't sure what he would tell her.

3.
How do you feel when you go to see a doctor when you're sick?

4. What were Tamika's symptoms?

   A. fever, broken arm, and cough

   B. cough, runny nose, and itchy skin

   C. cough, runny nose, and fever

   D. runny nose, fever, and sneezing

In Your Own Words

5. Write two other questions you can ask yourself about this passage.

   _____

   _____

   _____

   _____

5.
What were you curious about as you read this passage?

On Your Own!

Read this passage. Answer the questions that follow it.

Have you ever wondered why cats purr? No one really knows the answer for sure. Scientists study these animals to learn more about them. When kittens are a few days old, they learn to purr. Animal doctors called veterinarians think that this is a way for a kitten to talk to its mother. As a kitten grows, it continues to purr. Cats purr when they are happy or satisfied. They also purr when injured or in pain. Some veterinarians believe that purring helps cats heal themselves. Others believe that it may help repair bones.

A cat can purr when it lets out breath. A cat can also purr when it takes in breath. House cats are not the only cats that purr. Some big cats such as the bobcat, the cheetah, and the lynx also purr. Even bigger cats, such as the lion, sometimes make a sound that is like a purr, but is not actually a purring sound.

---

1. According to the passage, who studies cats to learn more about them?

   A. teachers

   B. scientists

   C. nurses

   D. children

2. What does a cat do to make a purring sound?

   A. wave its tail

   B. jump in the air

   C. breathe in or out

   D. scratch its ear

3. Kittens learn to purr when

   A. they are a few days old

   B. they are a few weeks old

   C. they are a few months old

   D. they are just born

4. What are animal doctors called?

   A. scientists

   B. surgeons

   C. cheetahs

   D. veterinarians

5. A cat purrs

   A. when it is threatened

   B. when it is happy

   C. when it is hungry

   D. when it is playing

6. Which cat does **not** actually make a purring sound?

   A. a cheetah

   B. a lynx

   C. a lion

   D. a bobcat

Write It Out   Use the passage to help you write a brief answer to the following question.

7. Do you have questions about cats? Write two questions of your own.

_____

_____

_____

_____

_____

_____

_____

_____

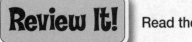

LESSON 7 — Main Idea

WORDS TO KNOW   **Main idea**   what most of the sentences in a passage or story are about. It is also the most important point that the author makes about a subject.

Review It!   Read these sentences. Use the Hint to find the main idea.

Spring is my favorite season. Everything seems to come alive. The flowers start to bloom, the birds start singing, and it starts to get warmer.

Hint   Think about what most of the sentences are about.

Try It!   Read the following passage. As you read, underline words that help you find the main idea.

(1) Lupe couldn't believe it was the first day of school already. It seemed as if she had just
(2) moved into her new neighborhood, but that was three months ago. Sometimes she
(3) wished she were back in her old neighborhood. Then she wouldn't be so nervous
(4) about starting school. Being in a new school meant she would be known as the "new
(5) kid." How long would that last? Until someone else new moved here, too? She was
(6) afraid she wouldn't make any friends. Not like Jenna and Kaya anyway. The three girls
(7) had been best friends since kindergarten. Now Lupe wouldn't see them every day, like
(8) she used to. She dragged herself up the stairs into school and entered her classroom.
(9) She saw a sign that said "Welcome New Students!" Maybe she wasn't going to be the
(10) only "new kid" after all!

Now, use the passage to answer the questions on the following page.

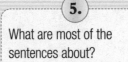

1. How long ago did Lupe move?

   A. two months

   B. three months

   C. four months

   D. five months

1.

Which sentence in the passage has this information?

2. How did Lupe know she wouldn't be the only "new kid" in her class?

   A. She saw a sign.

   B. She saw another new kid.

   C. She asked her teacher.

   D. She e-mailed her friends.

2.

What does Lupe see when she enters the classroom?

3. What is this story mainly about?

   A. a girl who doesn't want to make new friends

   B. a girl who is excited to go to a new school

   C. a girl who didn't like her old neighborhood

   D. a girl who moves to a new neighborhood

4. Another title of this passage could be

   A. "Jenna and Kaya Come to Visit"   C. "The New Kid"

   B. "Lupe's New Friends"   D. "Moving Day for Lupe"

In Your Own Words

5. Using your own words, write 2–3 sentences that tell the main idea of the passage.

5.

What are most of the sentences about?

_____

_____

_____

_____

On Your Own!

Read this passage. Answer the questions that follow it.

My family lives in a large city. There are ten children in my family. I am the youngest, which has its advantages and disadvantages.

The best part about being the youngest child is that I have nine people to look up to. My oldest sister is a doctor, and she helps children who are sick. One of my brothers is a teacher. He teaches sixth grade math. Another advantage I have is that I will always be the youngest. My brothers and sisters tease me about getting older, but I tell them that I will always be younger than they are!

There are a few disadvantages, though. One disadvantage is leftover clothing. I rarely ever get any new clothes, because I wear what my brothers grow out of. However, the worst part about being the youngest is being compared to all of my brothers and sisters who are good at everything. Teachers, coaches, and even doctors expect me to be just like my brothers and sisters.

I know I'm *not* just like them, and I think they know it, too. I'm *me*, and that's the way I like it!

---

1. According to the passage, what is the advantage of being the youngest child?

   A. always getting leftover clothes

   B. always getting teased

   C. always being younger than everyone else in the family

   D. always being compared to your sisters and brothers

2. According to the passage, one disadvantage of being the youngest of ten children is

   A. not getting new clothes

   B. looking up to older siblings

   C. always being the youngest

   D. having to take orders

3. What is this story mainly about?

   A. the best part about being the youngest child

   B. the advantages and disadvantages of being the youngest child

   C. the worst part about being the youngest child

   D. the advantages and disadvantages of being the oldest child

4. Another title of this passage could be

   A. "My Brothers and Sisters"

   B. "Getting New Clothes"

   C. "My Sister the Doctor"

   D. "The Youngest of Ten"

5. Which sentence from the story tells you that the narrator is happy being the youngest child?

   A. There are ten children in my family.

   B. However, the worst part about being the youngest is being compared to all of my brothers and sisters who are good at everything.

   C. I'm me, and that's the way I like it!

   D. I am the youngest, which has its advantages and disadvantages.

6. Which of the following is **not** a sentence that helps you find the main idea?

   A. I am the youngest, which has its advantages and disadvantages.

   B. My family lives in a large city.

   C. Another advantage I have is that I will always be the youngest.

   D. One disadvantage is leftover clothing.

Write It Out   Use the passage to help you write a brief answer to the following question.

7. Suppose you are a part of a large family. What might be an advantage of being the youngest? What might be a disadvantage?

_____

_____

_____

_____

8 Supporting Details

WORDS TO KNOW **Supporting details** pieces of information that tell about the main idea

Read these sentences. Use the Hint to find the details that support the main idea.

There are many reasons I love my dog. He likes to chase the ball when I throw it. He jumps up for his treats. He sits on command. Most of all, my dog loves me, too!

> **Hint** The main idea of the passage is that the writer loves his dog. Why does he love his dog? Think about the reasons or details he gives.

Read the following passage. As you read, <u>underline</u> phrases or sentences that contain details that support the main idea.

1 Porcupines are interesting animals. They live for about seven years. They eat insects,
2 frogs, lizards, mice, and birds' eggs. One of the most distinctive features of a porcupine
3 is its spines. Porcupines are born with these spines, but at birth they are soft and short.
4 As the porcupine grows, so do its spines. They become longer and sharper. The spines
5 are used to protect the porcupine. When an enemy approaches, a porcupine curls up
6 into a ball. The spines protect it from the enemy. The spines also protect a porcupine
7 when it falls. Sometimes porcupines use their spines as a sort of weapon. Because
8 they are not affected by poisons in some plants, they sometimes eat those plants. The
9 porcupines then lick their spines and spread sticky saliva on them. This sticky poison
10 fends off enemies.

Now, use the passage to answer the questions on the following page.

34

1. According to the passage, porcupines live for about

 A. six years   **C.** eight years

 B. seven years   **D.** nine years

2. Which of the following is **not** something porcupines eat?

 A. insects

 B. frogs

 C. squirrels

 D. mice

2.
Which animal is not included in the sentence about what porcupines eat?

3. When porcupines are born, their spines are—

 A. soft and short

 B. long and sharp

 C. soft and long

 D. short and sharp

3.
Which detail helps you answer this question? Where can you find this detail?

4. According to the passage, how does the porcupine use its spines?

 A. for decoration

 B. for entertainment

 C. for cleaning

 D. for protection

In Your Own Words

5. What main idea are the details in this passage supporting?

_____

_____

_____

_____

5.
What are all the sentences in the passage telling you about?

On Your Own!

Read this passage. Answer the questions that follow it.

Running for class president has taken a lot of hard work. First, I made a lot of campaign promises. I told my classmates that I would work to help keep the school grounds free from litter. I also said I would ask the principal to give us one "no homework day" each month. Then I made a lot of posters, T-shirts, and flyers with my name on them. My mom, my dad, and my little brother helped. Together we made 50 posters, 25 T-shirts, and over 100 flyers! Lastly, I went around and talked to a lot of the kids in my school. I wanted them to remember my name, Kate Hillman. My slogan was "Vote for Kate! She's great!"

On the day of the election, I was nervous. I wore my lucky charm and ate a good breakfast. I held my breath as the results were read over the loud speaker. Our principal, Mr. Kang, read each name carefully. Finally, he said my name. I had won! You can now call me "President Hillman."

1. For which position is Kate running?

   A. class president

   B. vice president

   C. orchestra president

   D. band president

2. Which of the following is a detail from the passage?

   A. Kate made buttons for her campaign.

   B. Kate talked with her teachers about her campaign.

   C. Kate didn't have a slogan for her campaign.

   D. Kate made promises for her campaign.

3. Kate was going to ask her principal for

   A. help making campaign posters

   B. litter-free school grounds

   C. one "no homework day" each month

   D. healthier food at the school cafeteria

4. Who read the results of the election?

   A. the principal

   B. Kate's mom

   C. Kate's dad

   D. the teacher

5. Which detail from the passage **best** shows you that Kate didn't have to do all the work on her own?

   A. My mom, my dad, and my little brother helped.

   B. Running for class president has taken a lot of hard work.

   C. I wore my lucky charm and ate a good breakfast.

   D. My slogan was "Vote for Kate. She's great!"

6. Which of the following is **not** a detail that supports the main idea of this passage?

   A. First, I made a lot of campaign promises.

   B. I held my breath as the results were read over the loud speaker.

   C. Lastly, I went around and talked to a lot of the kids in my school.

   D. Then I made a lot of posters, T-shirts, and flyers with my name on them.

Write It Out Use the passage to help you write a brief answer to the below question.

7. The first sentence, "Running for class president has taken a lot of hard work," is the main idea of the passage. Can you add one more detail that could support this main idea?

   _____

   _____

   _____

   _____

   _____

   _____

   _____

   _____

   _____

   _____

LESSON 9

Making Inferences

WORDS TO KNOW **Inferences** educated guesses based on what you're reading and what you already know. When you make an inference, you're figuring out something which the writer has not told you directly.

 Read these sentences. Use the Hint to help you understand the inference in the sentences.

Layla always buckles her seat belt in the car. She looks both ways before crossing the street. She wears a helmet when riding her bike.

> **Hint** Kayla is careful in everything she does. You can infer that she wants to stay safe.

 Read the following passage. As you read, <u>underline</u> sentences that suggest a meaning not directly stated in the passage.

(1) Brenda is a teacher. Her mother was also a teacher. Sometimes when Brenda was little, her mother brought her to see her classroom. Brenda liked to sit at her mother's desk and pretend that she was a teacher, too.

(2) Brenda's classroom is a fun place to be. She is funny, she helps the students do exciting projects, and she reads a lot of interesting books to them. Brenda dresses up when she reads stories. She also uses a different voice for each story character.

(3) When the end of the year arrives, Brenda's students are sad. They know they will miss their teacher. But they also know that she will be right across the hall.

Now, use the passage to answer the questions on the following page.

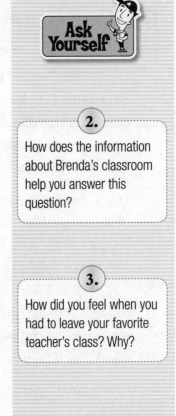

1. Based on the information in paragraph 1, what person **probably** influenced Brenda to become a teacher?

    A. her teacher   **C.** her principal

    B. her mother   **D.** her friend

2. Based on what you read in paragraph 2, you can infer that

    A. Brenda is a popular teacher

    B. Brenda does not enjoy teaching

    C. Brenda's classroom is boring

    D. Brenda's students dislike her

    > **2.**
    > How does the information about Brenda's classroom help you answer this question?

3. What is the **most likely** reason the students will miss Brenda?

    A. They will be moving to another building.

    B. They didn't like having her as a teacher.

    C. They can't wait for school to be over.

    D. They had fun in her class.

    > **3.**
    > How did you feel when you had to leave your favorite teacher's class? Why?

4. Based on the passage, what might Brenda's students be likely to do next year?

    A. move to another school

    B. dislike their teacher

    C. visit her classroom

    D. not come back to school

In Your Own Words

5. What can you infer about Brenda as a storyteller?

    _____

    _____

    _____

    _____

    > **5.**
    > How does Brenda tell stories? What does paragraph 2 tell you?

On Your Own!

Read this passage. Answer the questions that follow it.

Dan's older brother Pete was a dog trainer. He would often tell Dan about his job. Sometimes Pete trained dogs to listen to their owners. Sometimes he trained them to do tricks. One day Pete came home with exciting news. He was going to train a dog to work with a blind person. Dan got really curious and asked Pete if he could help. Pete told Dan that he could watch the training and learn.

Dan never forgot that day. He watched Pete carefully work with the dog and its owner. Soon Dan wanted to start training dogs himself. He first worked with puppies in his yard. Pete had told him that puppies are a little easier to train than full-grown dogs. Dan had to be patient, but he finally taught the puppies how to sit, stay, heel, and fetch. Then he started teaching them tricks. He taught one puppy how to jump through a hoop. He taught another how to balance a ball on its nose. Dan made sure he had plenty of treats on hand. Dan was so good with puppies that Pete asked him if he wanted to work at his company.

"Of course!" said Dan. Dan and Pete decided to name their company "From Puppy to Dog."

1. Why does Pete **most likely** tell Dan about his job?

   A. He wants to brag to Dan.
   B. He doesn't like his job.
   C. He doesn't like working with dogs.
   D. He is proud of his job.

2. You can infer that Dan **probably**

   A. doesn't care about Pete
   B. works hard in school
   C. looks up to Pete
   D. likes cats better than dogs

3. Based on the passage, you can infer that at first Dan trained puppies

   A. in an office

   B. from home

   C. from a farm

   D. with cats

4. Why did Dan teach the puppies how to sit, stay, heel, and fetch?

   A. He was asked by the owners to teach these skills to their pets.

   B. He didn't know how to teach them anything else.

   C. These are basic things a puppy should learn.

   D. These are harder skills for a puppy to learn.

5. What is the **most likely** reason Dan kept puppy treats on hand?

   A. He rewarded the puppies with treats while training them.

   B. He loved to eat them as a snack.

   C. He gave them to Pete to use.

   D. He often gets hungry while working with dogs.

6. Why did the brothers name their company "From Puppy to Dog"?

   A. They make gifts for puppies and dogs.

   B. They do not work with puppies.

   C. They only work with dogs.

   D. They work with puppies and dogs.

Write It Out   Use the passage to help you write a brief answer to the question below.

7. Why did Dan want to work for his older brother Pete?

_____

_____

_____

_____

_____

_____

_____

LESSON 10 — Drawing Conclusions

WORDS TO KNOW   **Conclusions**   ideas you get from clues in the passage, your own prior knowledge, and common sense

Review It!   Read these sentences. Use the Hint to help you draw a conclusion.

Marcus thought of everything for the party. He worked really hard to put it together for Keisha's special day. When Keisha arrived, she broke into a big smile.

> **Hint**   Based on what you read and what you already know, you can draw the conclusion that Keisha is very happy with Marcus for having planned a great party for her.

Try It!   Read the following passage. As you read, <u>underline</u> sentences that help you draw your conclusions.

1. The moon always looks different, but the moon itself does not really change. The moon gives off no light of its own. The white light we see is sunlight that reflects off its surface. When we see the moon in the sky, the lighted side is facing Earth.

2. The moon moves around Earth in a circle called an orbit. When you can't see the moon, this is called a new moon. A new moon occurs when the sun and the moon are on the same side of Earth. A full moon is seen when the sun and the moon are on opposite sides of Earth.

3. See if you can spot the moon. Can you tell which phase it is in? Many websites can show you how it will look each day of the year!

Now, use the passage to answer the questions on the following page.

1. When you see a new moon, you can conclude that

   A. the moon is moving away from Earth

   B. the sun and moon are on opposite sides of Earth

   C. the moon moves around Earth in an orbit

   D. the sun and moon are on the same side of Earth

1.

Which paragraph contains information on this topic? How can you use this information to draw your conclusion?

2. When you see a full moon, you can conclude that

   A. the moon is moving toward Earth

   B. the sun and moon are on opposite sides of Earth

   C. Earth moves around the moon in an orbit

   D. the sun and moon are on the same side of Earth

3. Based on the information in paragraph 1, the moon's surface

   A. is warm

   B. is hot

   C. is cold

   D. is reflective

4. Based on the information in the passage, you can conclude that

   A. the moon is beautiful to look at

   B. the moon looks different every day

   C. the moon changes twice a month

   D. the moon changes at the beginning of each month

4.

Picture the moon going around Earth. Would it look different to you day-to-day? How?

In Your Own Words

5. What conclusion can you draw about the moon after reading this passage?

   _____

   _____

   _____

5.

What information in the passage helps you draw a conclusion?

On Your Own!

Read this passage. Answer the questions that follow it.

As an actor, Christopher Reeve was best known for his role as Superman. Later in his life, he also became well known for his efforts to help others. Born in New York City in 1952, Reeve studied acting at a famous school of drama. At age 26, he starred in *Superman* and went on to make three more films about the hero. He was married to Dana Reeve and they had a son. Reeve also had two children from a previous relationship.

In 1985, Reeve began horseback riding. By 1989, he was competing. He also skied, canoed, and played tennis. He loved being outdoors. In 1995, Reeve was in a competition when he was thrown from his horse. He landed on his head and was paralyzed. He could not feel or move his body from the neck down. He could only breathe using a machine.

Reeve's brain worked just fine though, and he used it to tell people about spinal cord injuries. Just one year after the accident, the Reeves started a foundation. The Christopher and Dana Reeve Foundation helps pay for research on spinal cord injuries. It also works to improve the lives of people living with these injuries. Christopher Reeve died of heart failure in 2004. Sadly, in 2006, Dana Reeve also passed away. However, the foundation they started continues to help people in their honor.

1. Based on the passage, you can conclude that Christopher Reeve's career lasted

   A. about 10 years

   B. about 20 years

   C. more than 30 years

   D. less than 5 years

2. Which detail in the passage supports the conclusion that Christopher Reeve enjoyed sports?

   A. He also skied, canoed, and played tennis.

   B. Born in New York City in 1952, Reeve studied acting at a well-known school of drama.

   C. He loved being outdoors.

   D. He landed on his head and was paralyzed.

3. What can you conclude about spinal cord injuries?

   A. They do not hurt people.

   B. They can do a lot of damage.

   C. They do not happen very often.

   D. They are fun to have.

4. Based on the information in the passage, how would you describe Christopher Reeve?

   A. a trustworthy man

   B. a dishonest man

   C. a caring man

   D. a selfish man

5. What conclusion can you draw about Dana Reeve?

   A. She was not as caring as Christopher.

   B. She loved the outdoors as much as Christopher.

   C. She was not as honest as Christopher.

   D. She was just as caring as Christopher.

6. After reading the passage, what conclusion can you make about the Reeves?

   A. Christopher and Dana Reeve only thought of themselves.

   B. The Reeves started the foundation to help their son.

   C. In spite of their own difficulties, the Reeves tried to help others.

   D. The Reeves lived very happy and interesting lives.

Write It Out   Use the passage to help you write a brief answer to the question below.

7. What would the Reeves **most likely** be doing if they were still alive? Which clues from the passage help you draw your conclusion about their work?

_____

_____

_____

_____

_____

11 Fact and Opinion

WORDS TO KNOW **Fact** a statement that is true and can be proven
Opinion a statement that gives someone's feelings or beliefs about a topic. An opinion cannot be proven.

 Read these sentences. Use the Hint to help you identify facts and opinions.

Fred Rogers was a television personality. He hosted a children's show. He seemed like such a friendly person. I thought his show was very good for little children.

Hint The first two statements are facts. They can be proven. Clue words such as *seemed* and *thought* tell you that the last two statements are opinions.

 Read the following passage. As you read, <u>circle</u> details and clue words that help you identify facts and opinions.

1. People say all kinds of things. I think we shouldn't pay so much attention—most of the time, these things aren't true at all!

2. Here's an example. My cousin told me an ostrich buries its head in the sand when it's scared. That's not possible. If an ostrich buried its head, it wouldn't be able to breathe. An ostrich digs a hole for a nest. Sometimes the bird pokes its head in to check on the eggs. So it looks like it's burying its head!

3. Recently, my brother told me that touching a frog or toad will give you warts. The family medical dictionary says you cannot get warts from animals. My brother is so silly!

4. Do your research. Remember: you can't believe everything you hear.

Now, use the passage to answer the questions on the following page.

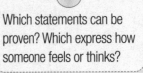

1. Which sentence from the passage expresses an opinion?

    A. An ostrich digs a hole as a nest.

    B. If an ostrich buried its head, it wouldn't be able to breathe.

    C. The family medical dictionary says you cannot get warts from animals.

    D. Do your research.

2. Which of the following statements is a fact?

    A. The family medical dictionary says you cannot get warts from animals.

    B. My brother is so silly!

    C. That's not possible.

    D. I think we shouldn't pay so much attention—most of the time, these things aren't true at all!

    2. Which statement can be proven? Where can you check this fact?

3. It can be proven that

    A. a scared ostrich buries its head in the sand

    B. an ostrich makes a nest in the water

    C. an ostrich doesn't lay eggs

    D. an ostrich pokes its head in the sand to check on its eggs

    3. Which statement can you check in an encyclopedia?

4. Which of the following statements tells what someone feels?

    A. Here's an example.
    B. My brother is so silly!

    C. Do your research.
    D. The family medical dictionary says you cannot get warts from animals.

In Your Own Words

5. Write one fact and one opinion from the passage.

    _____

    _____

    _____

    _____

    5. Which statements can be proven? Which express how someone feels or thinks?

On Your Own!

Read this passage. Answer the questions that follow it.

I'm hoping the city board doesn't close the Old Oak Theater. It's the best theater in town! It is on Oak Street, right behind the library. It has the most comfortable seats around. There are six different theaters. That means there's always a good movie playing.

I love it because you can really relax and enjoy yourself at the Oak Theater. For instance, there's the big popcorn combo. You get a large popcorn and a large drink for only three dollars. What a bargain! You even get free refills on your drink. The theaters show fun previews before each movie. A preview is a sneak peek at a movie that will be coming out soon. Best of all, they don't show too many of them. I hate waiting too long for the movie to start. The perfect place to sit is on the very last row at the top. That's where you get the very best view.

The theater is really good about keeping up with new movies coming out. This week the theater is playing a brand-new movie. It's a movie my friends and I have been waiting to see. I would go to the Oak Theater every day if I could. So should you! So again, I'm hoping the city understands how important this theater is. It's not just nice for kids, it's good for the whole town.

1. **Which of the following statements is an opinion?**

   A. I love it because you can really relax and enjoy yourself at the Oak Theater.

   B. There are six different theaters.

   C. It is on Oak Street, right behind the library.

   D. This week the theater is playing a brand-new movie.

2. **Which of the following statements is a fact?**

   A. I hate waiting too long for the movie to start.

   B. It's the best theater in town!

   C. That's where you get the very best view.

   D. You get a large popcorn and a large drink for only three dollars.

3. In which of the following statements is the writer giving a fact?

   A. That's where you get the very best view.

   B. You even get free refills on your drink.

   C. It has the most comfortable seats around.

   D. I would go to the Oak Theater every day if I could.

4. In which of the following statements is the writer expressing an opinion?

   A. A preview is a sneak peek at a movie that will be coming out soon.

   B. The theaters show fun previews before each movie.

   C. This week the theater is playing a brand-new movie.

   D. It has the most comfortable seats around.

5. Which of the following statements **cannot** be proven?

   A. For instance, there's the big popcorn combo.

   B. What a bargain!

   C. There are six different theaters.

   D. You get a large popcorn and a large drink for only three dollars.

6. Which of the following statements **can** be proven?

   A. That means there's always a good movie playing.

   B. That's where you get the very best view.

   C. It is on Oak Street, right behind the library.

   D. Best of all, they don't show too many of them.

Write It Out Use the passage to help you write a brief answer to the question below.

7. Have you seen a movie recently at a theater or on TV? Would you recommend it to a friend? Why?

_____

_____

_____

_____

_____

LESSON 12 Summarizing

WORDS TO KNOW **Summarizing** giving the main idea and important details of the text in your own words

Review It! Read these sentences. Use the Hint to help you summarize it.

I have a lizard. His name is Lenny. He is green and brown. I keep him in an aquarium that has rocks on the bottom. He likes to climb on the rocks.

Hint Think about the details the author gives about his pet lizard. Which details are important? Which are not? This will help you summarize the paragraph.

Try It! Read the following passage. As you read, <u>underline</u> sentences that tell the main idea and important details.

1. Most people do not think about taking care of their eyes. We use our eyes every day.
2. Good eye care is important. Here are some tips for caring for your eyes. Have a doctor
3. check your eyes every year. Eye exams do not take long, and they do not hurt. Some
4. parts of the exam can be uncomfortable because you may not be used to them. Wear
5. eyeglasses or contact lenses if the doctor thinks that you need them. Eat right, exercise,
6. and sleep. Never look directly into the sun. The eyes are made to see only certain types
7. of light. The sun is too bright for the eyes to handle, so wear sunglasses on bright days.
8. Make sure there is plenty of light when you read. You only have one pair of eyes. Take
9. care of them, and they will help take care of you!

Now, use the passage to answer the questions on the following page.

1. This passage is about

   A. going to the eye doctor   **C.** taking care of your eyes

   B. eating right   **D.** picking out sunglasses

2. Which sentence below belongs in a summary of the passage?

   A. We use our eyes every day.

   B. Have a doctor check your eyes every year.

   C. You only have one pair of eyes.

   D. Eye exams do not take long, and they do not hurt.

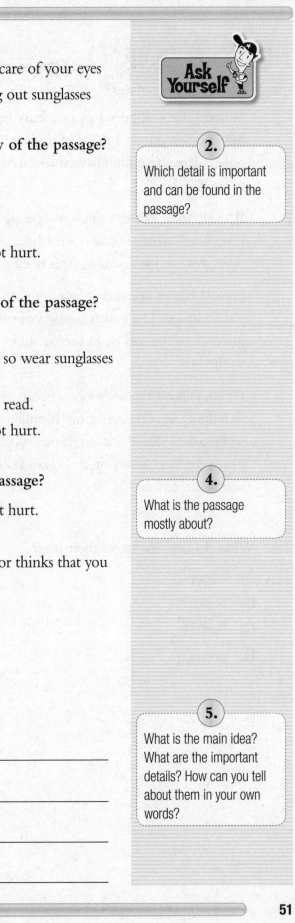

Ask Yourself

2.
Which detail is important and can be found in the passage?

3. Which sentence would **not** help a summary of the passage?

   A. Eat right, exercise, and sleep.

   B. The sun is too bright for the eyes to handle, so wear sunglasses on bright days.

   C. Make sure there is plenty of light when you read.

   D. Eye exams do not take long, and they do not hurt.

4. Which sentence gives the main idea of the passage?

   A. Eye exams do not take long and they do not hurt.

   B. Good eye care is important.

   C. Wear eyeglasses or contact lenses if the doctor thinks that you need them.

   D. Here are some tips for caring for your eyes.

4.
What is the passage mostly about?

In Your Own Words

5. Summarize the passage in your own words.

   _____

   _____

   _____

   _____

5.
What is the main idea? What are the important details? How can you tell about them in your own words?

On Your Own!

Read this passage. Answer the questions that follow it.

When I think of bees, I picture busy hives and little creatures buzzing around flowers. Sometimes I think of stingers! But I certainly don't think about baskets of pollen. Bees have little baskets to carry pollen. This is very important to nature and to us. Why?

Bees fly from flower to flower looking for nectar and pollen. Nectar is a food that gives bees energy. It is also what bees use to make honey. Pollen is a food that helps bees grow and stay strong. Bees need nectar and pollen to live.

Female honey bees have something on their legs that no other insects have. It's a pollen basket. The basket is made of stiff hairs. When a bee visits a flower, she pushes pollen into the basket, and some sticks to the hairs. Then she carries the pollen back to the hive.

Pollen falls off the bee's legs when it visits other flowers. This is an important step in helping new flowers grow. If pollen was not moved from one flower to another, some plants would die out. If plants died out, people would die out, too. People need plants for food, clean air, and clean water. Bees help move pollen, so they help people and plants to live.

---

1. What do bees carry on their legs?

    A. honey

    B. pollen

    C. flowers

    D. nectar

2. Pollen is a food that

    A. gives bees energy

    B. is made of stiff hairs

    C. helps bees grow

    D. bees do not like

3. What happens to pollen when a bee visits flowers?

    A. It becomes dry and stiff.

    B. It is lost.

    C. It falls off the bee's legs.

    D. It is dropped on the ground.

4. Which sentence gives the main idea of the passage?

    A. When I think of bees, I picture busy hives and little creatures buzzing around flowers.

    B. Bees have little baskets to carry pollen.

    C. Bees help move pollen, so they help people and plants to live.

    D. Pollen falls off the bee's legs when it visits other flowers.

5. Which sentence has important details that should be included in a summary of the passage?

    A. I picture busy hives and little creatures buzzing around flowers.

    B. If pollen was not moved from one flower to another, some plants would die out.

    C. This is an important step in helping new flowers grow.

    D. The basket is made of stiff hairs.

6. A sentence that does **not** belong in a summary of the passage is

    A. If plants died out, people would die out, too.

    B. This is very important to nature and to us.

    C. Bees help move pollen, so they help people and plants to live.

    D. Sometimes I think of stingers!

Write It Out   Use the passage to help you write a brief answer to the question below.

7. How would you summarize this passage? Write a 3-4 sentence summary of the passage.

_____

_____

_____

_____

_____

_____

LESSON 13 — Sequence

WORDS TO KNOW
Sequence the order in which events take place. Sequence is also called time order or chronological order.

Review It!

Read these sentences. Use the Hint to help you figure out the sequence.

Going to the zoo was so much fun! First, we saw the lions. Then we saw the giraffes. After lunch, we went to see the elephants. It was a great day!

Hint Look for the word clues *first, then*, and *after* to figure out the order in which the author saw the different animals at the zoo: lions, giraffes, elephants.

Try It!

Read the following passage. As you read, <u>circle</u> word clues that help you figure out the order in which events take place.

1 I had a lot of fun this summer. In June, I went to day camp. We played games. We swam
2 every day. On the first day of camp, I met Karina. We became good friends. One day, we
3 made friendship bracelets. On the last day, we promised to write to each other! In July,
4 my family went to Oklahoma. We visited my grandmother, who lives on a farm. I got
5 to help her on the farm. First we fed the animals. Then we picked some blueberries and
6 made them into jam. Grandma gave us some of the jam to take home. It tastes great!
7 Now it is August and I am back home and ready to go back to school. I want to meet
8 my new teacher. I'm not sure who will be in my class, but I'm sure I'll have fun.

Now, use the passage to answer the questions on the following page.

1. During the summer, where did the author go **first**?

   A. to school

   B. to day camp

   C. to her grandma's house

   D. to her friend's house

2. What did the author do **first** on her grandmother's farm?

   A. She made jam.

   B. She picked blueberries.

   C. She took some jam home.

   D. She fed the animals.

3. The **last** thing the author did at camp in June was

   A. go swimming

   B. make friendship bracelets

   C. promise she would write to her friend

   D. play games

4. What did the author do after she left her grandmother's farm?

   A. She went back home.   C. She went back to school.

   B. She took a trip.   D. She visited a friend.

In Your Own Words

5. What did the author do at her grandmother's farm? List the events in sequence, or chronological order.

_____

_____

_____

_____

Ask Yourself

1. Which sentence includes information about the month of June?

2. What is the order of events in July?

5. What clue words help you figure out the sequence?

On Your Own! Read this passage. Answer the questions that follow it.

On December 1, 1955, an African American woman named Rosa Parks boarded a bus in Alabama and sat down near the front. At the next stop, some white riders boarded. One man was looking for a seat. "Hey!" the bus driver yelled to Parks. "Move to the back!" At that time in Alabama, only white riders got to sit near the front of the bus. But Parks did not give up her seat.

"Just give him your seat," the driver urged. Rosa Parks disagreed. She felt that when African Americans gave in, they were treated worse. "I'll have you arrested," the driver said. "You may do that," she said. At the next stop, policemen took her to the city jail.

News of Parks's arrest spread. African Americans became angry. They had had enough. Lawyers for Parks wanted to prove that what had happened to her was illegal. They took her case all the way to the Supreme Court. African Americans started refusing to ride the buses. Without them, the bus company lost money. African Americans were pressured to ride the buses again, but they still refused.

The court agreed with Rosa Parks. It said that what had happened to her on the bus was illegal. All people had the right to ride the buses and sit in any seat they want.

1. According to the passage, what happened after Rosa Parks boarded the bus and sat down?

   A. The bus driver yelled at her.
   B. She got arrested.
   C. Some white riders got on the bus.
   D. She refused to give up her seat.

2. The bus driver yelled at Rosa Parks

   A. when she got on the bus
   B. when she was getting off the bus
   C. before an African American rider boarded
   D. after some white riders boarded

3. After the bus driver told Rosa Parks that he would have her arrested

    A. some white riders boarded the bus

    B. she told him that he could do that

    C. she got off the bus

    D. she gave up her seat

4. After the police arrested Rosa Parks, they took her

    A. back to her home

    B. back to the bus station

    C. to the city jail

    D. to the Supreme Court

5. After the news of Rosa Parks's arrest spread

    A. African Americans refused to ride the buses

    B. African Americans stood on buses

    C. white riders stood on buses

    D. white riders refused to ride the buses

6. What happened after the Supreme Court made its decision?

    A. African Americans still had to give up their seats.

    B. Rosa Parks led a protest about her stay in jail.

    C. White riders had to stand when they rode a bus.

    D. All people had the right to sit in any seat on a bus.

Write It Out   Use the information in the passage to fill in the sequence chart.

7.

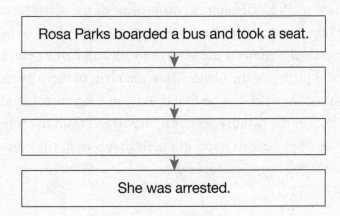

Rosa Parks boarded a bus and took a seat.

↓

↓

↓

She was arrested.

LESSON 14 Cause and Effect

WORDS TO KNOW **Cause and effect**   A **cause** is the reason something happens and the **effect** is the result of a cause.

 Read these sentences. Use the Hint to help you figure out the cause and effect.

Kelly forgot to set her alarm clock. The next morning, she woke up late. She missed the bus. She was late for school and missed her first class.

> **Hint**   Many things happened to Kelly one morning. What caused them?

 Read the following passage. As you read, <u>circle</u> details that show cause and effect.

1   Christmas Island is in the Indian Ocean. An explorer named the island on Christmas
2   Day in 1643. The Christmas Island National Park covers over 60 percent of the island.
3   The park opened in 1980. Before that, many areas of the island were being damaged
4   because of mining. The government set aside part of the island to help save its natural
5   resources. The park also protects the plants and animals that live on the island. There are
6   over 400 kinds of plants on the island. More than half of them produce flowers. Some
7   of the plants that grow there can be found only on Christmas Island. Over 100 million
8   red crabs also live on the island. Every year, they travel from the forest to the beach to
9   have their babies. They have to travel in the morning or in the evening. If they travel at
10   midday, when it is too hot, they could die.

Now, use the passage to answer the questions on the following page.

1. How did Christmas Island get its name?

   A. People opened presents.

   B. It was named on Christmas Day.

   C. It was explored by a man named Christmas.

   D. The island is red and green.

2. What caused damage to many areas of the island?

   A. mining   C. pollution

   B. litter   D. weather

   2. Which clue words help you find the cause?

3. What causes the red crabs to travel to the beach every year?

   A. They don't like the forest.

   B. They like to travel.

   C. They go there to have their babies.

   D. They want to swim.

   3. Which detail helps you find the cause?

4. Traveling during midday could cause the crabs

   A. to be unable to swim

   B. to die

   C. to have babies

   D. to not have babies

In Your Own Words

5. Write one effect of opening the Christmas Island National Park.

   5. Why was the park opened?

   _____

   _____

   _____

   _____

On Your Own!

Read this passage. Answer the questions that follow it.

Long, long ago, spiders weren't good at spinning webs. They could make sticky thread, but they weren't able to make the threads stretch across large spaces. Some spiders fell and hurt themselves while trying to jump from one place to another. Well, here's the story about how that changed.

One day, Grandpa Spider was gazing at a tiny, beautiful leaf. He had just picked it up when a gust of wind came along. It blew so hard the leaf flew right out of his hand and across the tree where Grandpa was sitting. It landed on another branch. This gave Grandpa an idea!

The next day, Grandpa Spider was sitting on a railing. He spun some sticky thread. He held the thread up in the air and waited for some wind. Then he let go of the thread. The wind grabbed it and carried it to another part of the railing where it stuck. His plan worked! He waited for more wind and made a few more spokes for his web.

From that day forward, spiders knew that if they wanted to build strong, beautiful webs, they had to wait for a windy day!

1. **What caused some spiders to fall and hurt themselves?**

    A. They were trying to catch flies.

    B. They were trying to jump across large areas.

    C. They were trying to spin thread.

    D. They were trying to sleep.

2. **According the second paragraph, why did the leaf fly across the tree?**

    A. Grandpa threw it.

    B. The leaf landed on a branch.

    C. The wind blew.

    D. An insect carried it.

3. What was the effect of the wind blowing the leaf off of Grandpa's branch?

   A. The leaf flew across the tree and landed on another branch.

   B. The leaf flew out of the tree and landed on the ground.

   C. The leaf flew into the air and landed in a web.

   D. The leaf flew out of the tree and into another spider's hand.

4. Grandpa let go of the thread because

   A. he felt the wind coming up

   B. he became scared

   C. he couldn't hold on any longer

   D. he got really tired

5. What was the effect of Grandpa's hard work?

   A. The wind blew his web apart.

   B. He found another leaf.

   C. He spun a strong, beautiful web.

   D. He was blown out of the tree.

6. Grandpa Spider's story explains

   A. why spiders spin webs

   B. why spiders like to jump from tree to tree

   C. why spiders like leaves

   D. why spiders build their webs on windy days

Write It Out   Use the story to help you complete the chart below with causes and effects.

7.

Cause	Effect

LESSON
15 Compare and Contrast

WORDS TO KNOW **Compare and contrast** show how things are alike and different

---

 Read these sentences. Use the Hint to help you compare and contrast.

Jade has green eyes and brown hair. Her brother Danny has brown eyes and brown hair. They both like to ride their bikes. Jade's bike is red and Danny's bike is blue.

> **Hint** Jade and Danny are both alike and different. Think about the ways they are alike. What ways are they different?

 Read the following passage. As you read, <u>underline</u> details that help you compare and contrast.

(1) My sisters are two of my best friends. My older sister Meg is a great role model. She is
(2) in college and she gets good grades. She has a part-time job, and she helps my parents
(3) pay for her books. My younger sister Ellen is also a great role model. She helps at the
(4) local animal shelter. She helps take care of the pets in our neighborhood.

(5) Both of my sisters like music. Meg likes to listen to rock music. Ellen likes country
(6) music. They both like to watch TV. Ellen watches shows that are funny, while Meg
(7) watches the news programs.

(8) I enjoy spending time with my sisters. Sometimes the three of us go to a movie. The
(9) only problem is deciding who gets to choose which one!

Now, use the passage to answer the questions on the following page.

1. **What is one way Meg and Ellen are alike?**

   A. They both go to college.

   B. They both like animals.

   C. They both are good role models.

   D. They both dislike movies.

2. **Both Meg and Ellen like**

   A. books

   B. music

   C. animals

   D. painting

3. **What is one way Meg and Ellen are different?**

   A. They go to different schools.

   B. They live in different states.

   C. They like different kinds of TV shows.

   D. They like to eat different foods.

4. **Meg likes rock music, while Ellen likes**

   A. opera   C. classical

   B. pop   D. country

In Your Own Words

5. **Write how Meg and Ellen are different in the way they help.**

   _____

   _____

   _____

Ask Yourself

2. What is one thing both sisters like?

3. What kind of television shows do the sisters like to watch?

5. Who does Meg help? Who does Ellen help?

On Your Own!

Read this passage. Answer the questions that follow it.

Is it better to save money at home or at a bank? Some people prefer to save money at home. Some people think it is safer to keep money in a bank. At home, some people save money in a piggy bank or under a mattress. At home, you know exactly where the money is. When you save money at a bank, you are trusting the bank to keep the money safe.

One problem with keeping money at home is that it cannot be replaced if something happens to it. For example, suppose there is a fire. The money will be lost forever. Money stored in a bank is very safe. It is kept in a giant locked vault. There are also laws to make sure that a bank will return any money you save there.

A bank might also pay you for saving your money. How can you earn money while saving money? Here's how. Banks lend money to people all the time. The money gets paid back little by little. The total money that people pay a bank is more than the amount they borrowed. The difference between what customers pay the bank and what they borrowed is called interest. A bank gives some of the interest to people who have savings accounts. The larger the account, the more interest you get. No matter how you choose to save money, it is one way to prepare for the future.

1. What is one thing you know when you save money at home that you don't know when you save it at a bank?

    A. the amount of money other people have

    B. where it is

    C. the amount other people invest

    D. what other customers think of the bank

2. One problem with saving money at home that is **not** a problem at a bank is

    A. you earn interest on your money

    B. there are laws to protect your money

    C. your money cannot be replaced if something happens to it

    D. you have to pay money back

3. Some people save money at home in a piggy bank, while money at a bank is stored in

   A. a locked vault

   B. a wooden safe

   C. a special bag

   D. a large plastic box

4. What is one advantage you have saving at a bank over saving at home?

   A. A bank might charge you fees to save money.

   B. A bank stores your money in a huge piggy bank.

   C. A bank might loan your money to others.

   D. A bank might pay you interest on your money.

5. Unlike money you save at home, your money saved at a bank

   A. will double in a few years

   B. does not earn interest

   C. is protected by law, in case it is lost

   D. will not be safe

6. According to the passage, what is one way saving money at home and at a bank are alike?

   A. Money is safe in both places.

   B. Both help you prepare for the future.

   C. You can earn interest in both places.

   D. There are piggy banks at both places.

Write It Out   Use the passage to help you complete the chart below.

7.

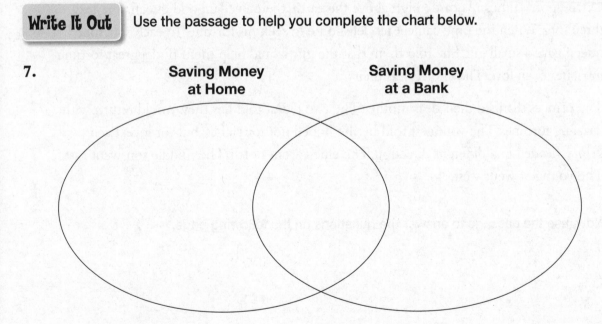

Saving Money at Home   Saving Money at a Bank

LESSON 16 Genres

WORDS TO KNOW

Genres different types of literature. The main genres are fiction, poetry, drama, and nonfiction. Fiction includes different kinds of made-up stories, such as fairy tales. Poetry has short lines and is written in stanzas. Sometimes it rhymes. Drama uses dialogue and stage directions.

Review It! Read the lines below. Use the Hint to figure out the genre.

Roses are red, violets are blue.
Sugar is sweet, and so are you!

> **Hint** Use the rhyming words *blue* and *you* at the end of lines as clues to the genre.

Try It! Read the passage. As you read, <u>underline</u> the words or phrases that help you figure out the genre.

1. Once upon a time, in a castle high above the earth, there lived a good queen. She had three sons. When the time came, each left home to seek his fortune. To each son, the queen gave a small gift. She told them that the gift would help them find a great fortune in riches or in love. The choice was theirs.

2. The princes thanked their dear mother. The two eldest told her they would return with dazzling fortunes. The youngest told her he hoped not for riches, but for love. Each prince headed in a different direction. The eldest went north. The middle son went east. The youngest went west.

Now, use the passage to answer the questions on the following page.

Reading Literature

1. What type of passage is this?

   A. fiction

   B. drama

   C. poetry

   D. history

1.

What words and phrases help you figure out the genre?

2. Which phrase **best** helps you identify the type of passage?

   A. in a castle high above the earth

   B. had three sons

   C. gave each a small gift

   D. youngest went west

3. Which narrows the genre to a more specific kind of writing?

   A. news report   C. ghost story

   B. biography   D. fairy tale

4. A clue that helps you narrow the genre is

   A. each son left home

   B. the youngest son hoped for love

   C. once upon a time

   D. each son headed in a different direction

4.

Do any words or phrases look very familiar?

In Your Own Words

5. Write a title for the passage that helps the reader predict what the story will be about.

   _____

   _____

   _____

   _____

5.

What kinds of words in the title will make sure readers have an idea of what they will read?

Reading Literature

Reading Literature

Characters

Max, age seven   **Jane**, age five   **Mother**

All are outside in their yard. Jane is digging a hole with a small shovel.

Max: (*pointing to Jane*) Mother! What is she doing?

Mother: Well, it looks like she is digging holes in the yard.

Max: (*looking puzzled*) Now what is she doing?

Mother: She appears to be putting ice cubes in the holes.

Max: Why would she do that?

Mother: Let's find out. You ask her.

Max: Jane, why are you putting ice in the holes?

Jane: My teacher told us Earth is too hot. I thought some ice might help it cool down.

Mother: That's a lovely thought, dear. But that's not how to we can help Earth cool down. But there is something we can do. Let's plant a tree!

---

1. What is the genre of this writing?

   A. fiction

   B. drama

   C. poetry

   D. none of the above

2. Who is the first speaker?

   A. Mother

   B. Max

   C. Jane

   D. Jane's teacher

3. How does the writing help you know who is speaking?

   A. list of characters

   B. quotation marks

   C. underlined names

   D. names are in bold type

4. In the writing, who has the most dialogue?

   A. Mother

   B. Max

   C. Jane

   D. Jane's teacher

5. Who does most of the action in this writing?

   A. Max

   B. Mother

   C. Jane

   D. Father

6. From the list of characters, you learn

   A. only that Jane is older than Max

   B. only that Max is older than Jane

   C. all the characters are children

   D. the characters are Jane, Max, and Mother

Write It Out   Which character will speak next? What will he or she say? Write a line of dialogue for that character.

7. _____

   _____

   _____

   _____

   _____

   _____

   _____

   _____

Author's Purpose

WORDS TO KNOW   **Author's purpose**   the reason or reasons an author has for writing. Authors often write to entertain, teach or tell something, or affect how a reader feels about something.

 Read these sentences below. Use the Hint to figure out the author's purpose.

The crazy scientist crossed an ape and a flower. He called it a chim-pansy!

Hint   The word *chim-pansy* is a pun on the words *chimpanzee*, an ape, and *pansy*, a flower. If you smiled or giggled when you read the passage, you know why the author wrote it.

 Read this story. As you read, <u>underline</u> the words and phrases that help you figure out the author's purpose.

1. The alarm went off at 4:00 A.M. Mom and I got into the van half an hour later. There were six others in the van. They nodded as we climbed in. It was too early to talk.

2. We drove for half an hour into the desert. It was still dark. It should have been quiet, but it wasn't. A loud roar came from the center of the camp. Flames shot out of huge burners. I thought the yards of fabric would catch on fire, but instead they filled with air and grew bigger.

3. When everything was ready, we got in. There was standing room only. Then we took off. We were flying over the desert in a hot air balloon. What a sight below us!

Now, use the story to answer the questions on the following page.

Reading Literature

1. From the story, you can tell that the author is

    A. the van driver

    B. the mother

    C. the person who is telling the story

    D. the hot air balloon pilot

Ask Yourself

1.
Which pronoun is used most often in the passage?

2. What feeling do you think the author wants you to have when reading the second paragraph?

    A. happy   **C.** bored

    B. scared   **D.** angry

3. How do you think the author wants you to feel at the end of the story?

    A. bored   **C.** tired

    B. scared   **D.** excited

4. The author's purpose for writing the passage is to

    A. give directions to a hot-air balloon camp

    B. tell about the desert

    C. explain how hot air balloons work

    D. entertain by sharing a personal experience

4.
Is the author trying to inform, persuade, or entertain?

In Your Own Words

5. Write a title for the story that gives the reader a hint to the author's purpose.

_____

_____

_____

5.
What words in your title will help readers know the author's purpose?

Reading Literature

On Your Own!

Read this passage. Answer the questions that follow it.

You walk toward the playground. You hear, "Apples, berries, grapes, and plums. Tell us when your birthday comes…" Then you hear a slapping sound. The song is a jump rope rhyme. The slapping sound is a jump rope hitting the ground. You see the jumper enter the rope on "comes." She jumps once for each month. You watch her jump out after naming her birthday month.

Once, skipping rope was just a game for girls. Not any more. Boxers skip rope as part of their training. Runners skip rope to warm up for a race. Jumping rope is a good workout. Jumping gets the heart going.

One jump rope is good. Two jump ropes are even better! The two jump rope game is called Double Dutch. The spinners turn one rope to the left. They turn the other rope to the right. The jumper hops over one rope and then quickly over the other.

In 1973 David W. Walker turned the street game of Double Dutch into a world-class sport. It is a team sport. The first tournament, in 1974, had 600 boys and girls. More than 100,000 kids enter Double Dutch meets all over the world.

1. **Read these sentences from the passage.**

   "Apples, berries, grapes, and plums. Tell us when your birthday comes…"

   The author might have included these sentences to

   A. explain who David W. Walker is

   B. show that girls are the best jumpers

   C. introduce the topic in a way the reader may know

   D. illustrate that boys don't know how to play jump rope

2. **Read these sentences from the passage.**

   The spinners turn one rope to the left. They turn the other rope to the right. The jumper hops over one rope and then quickly over the other.

   The author included this information to

   A. name the different positions in Double Dutch

   B. tell where the rope spinners stand in Double Dutch

   C. explain what the rope spinners do in Double Dutch

   D. show the reader how difficult Double Dutch is

3. The author's purpose for including information about David W. Walker is to

   A. tell who founded the Double Dutch sport

   B. name the author of the passage

   C. introduce a sports writer

   D. explain how Walker makes jump ropes

4. The passage is mostly about

   A. the history of games girls play

   B. funny jump rope rhymes

   C. David Walker's life

   D. the history of jumping rope

5. From the passage, you can tell that the author thinks jumping rope is

   A. only for girls

   B. safe for boxers

   C. good exercise

   D. not really a sport

6. The author's purpose for writing the passage is to

   A. make the reader laugh

   B. tell how to make jump rope

   C. get the reader to exercise

   D. give information about jumping rope

Write It Out   Tell what the most interesting or surprising thing you read in the passage was.

7. _____

   _____

   _____

   _____

   _____

   _____

   _____

Reading Literature

WORDS TO KNOW

Plot what happens in a story. A plot includes a problem or conflict that the main character or characters must try to solve.

Reading Literature

Review It!

Read these sentences to figure out the plot.

People in the village whispered that the house on the hill was haunted. But was it? Juan had to find out for himself.

> **Hint** Here, the phrase *had to find out for himself* helps you understand the problem Juan will try to solve.

Try It!

Read this story. As you read, underline the words and phrases that help you figure out the plot.

(1) Dog was carrying a large bone in his mouth. He was so pleased with himself. "This is the biggest bone in the world!" he thought. Dog was eager to get home. He decided to try a shortcut across a stream.

(2) "This is indeed my lucky day," thought Dog at the river's edge. A thick log reached from one bank of the stream to the other. As Dog walked on the log, he looked down. There in the water, staring at him, was another dog with a bone even bigger than his!

(3) "I want THAT bone!" cried Dog. He opened his mouth to grab the bigger bone and his bone fell into the stream and sank. He realized he was looking at his reflection in the water. Feeling sad, Dog slowly walked home.

Now, use the story to answer the questions on the following page.

1. The plot in this story begins with Dog

    A. carrying a stick   **C.** digging up a huge bone

    B. crossing a stream   **D.** carrying a large bone

1.

What is the first thing that happens in the story?

2. How does Dog feel at the beginning of the story?

    A. greedy   **C.** jealous

    B. proud   **D.** silly

3. What problem does Dog think he needs to solve?

    A. He cannot cross the stream.

    B. The bone is too heavy to carry.

    C. He needs to get the other dog's bone.

    D. He wants to find a new way home.

4. Dog tries to solve the problem by

    A. grabbing the bigger bone

    B. not taking the shortcut

    C. swimming across the stream

    D. floating the bone in the stream

4.

What does Dog do when he looks down in the stream?

In Your Own Words

5. Explain why Dog feels the way he does at the end of the story.

_____

_____

_____

_____

_____

5.

What happens at the end of the story?

Reading Literature

On Your Own!

Read this story. Answer the questions that follow it.

Old Turtle lived by a lake with two friends, Big Goose and Little Goose. The friends liked to talk and talk about their life experiences. Then one year, the lake began to dry up. Old Turtle and the geese could talk of nothing else. One day Big Goose said, "Old Turtle, we must leave this lake. We have seen great lakes over the mountains where there is much water."

Old Turtle said, "Please take me with you!"

But how? The friends talked and talked. Big Goose said, "We will carry a strong stick between us with our bills. And you must hold onto the stick with your strong jaws. But if you open your mouth, you will fall to the earth!"

Old Turtle clamped his jaws around the stick. Up, up, flew the three friends. Old Turtle looked down on the trees and village children playing outdoors. The children had never seen a turtle fly! "Did you ever see anything so silly?" they laughed.

"Silly?" said Old Turtle. When he opened his mouth to say this, poor Old Turtle let go of the stick and fell to the earth.

---

1. Who are the characters facing the problem in the story?

   A. Old Turtle

   B. Big Goose and Little Goose

   C. Old Turtle, Big Goose, and Little Goose

   D. Old Turtle and Big Goose

2. What is the problem the characters face in the story?

   A. how to get along

   B. how to live a long time

   C. how to learn to fly

   D. how to take Old Turtle to the new lakes

3. What idea do the geese have to solve the problem?

   A. carry a stick for Old Turtle to hold onto

   B. find a path Old Turtle can walk on

   C. try to teach Old Turtle to fly

   D. leave Old Turtle and fly away

4. The geese's solution doesn't work out because

   A. the geese do not have strong enough bills

   B. Old Turtle opens his mouth

   C. Old Turtle has strong jaws

   D. Old Turtle gets tired

5. Which of the following is **not** a part of the plot in the story?

   A. Old Turtle cannot see the tops of trees from the lake.

   B. The lake over the mountains is very deep.

   C. The geese want to help their friend.

   D. The laughing children make Old Turtle angry.

6. How does the plot end in the story?

   A. The friends live happily ever after in the new lake.

   B. Old Turtle goes to live with the village children.

   C. Old Turtle lets go of the stick and falls to Earth.

   D. The geese walk to the new lake with Old Turtle.

Write It Out   How can you change the plot so that it has a happy ending? Write a few sentences to tell about the new ending.

7. _____

   _____

   _____

   _____

   _____

   _____

Reading Literature

| WORDS TO KNOW | **Characters** the main people or animals in a story. Characters have traits that make them act and speak in certain ways. |

Review It! Read these sentences and identify the main character.

The bus driver smiled as two men, followed by three school children, boarded his bus. An elderly woman appeared at the door. "Let me help you," said the driver offering his hand.

Hint The bus driver smiles and wants to help the elderly woman. He is the character you learn the most about in this story.

Try It! Read this story. As you read, underline the names of the characters and circle the word that help you figure out the characters' traits.

(1) Wendy took good care of Fred and Ginger, her cats. While they ate their breakfast, she cleaned the litter box. Wendy's brother Rick never helped out because of his allergies.

(2) One spring day, Wendy put on her new jacket, shut the coat closet, and grabbed her book bag. Ready to leave, Wendy knelt to scratch Fred. Then she looked at her watch and thought, "I'm going to be late!" But she couldn't leave yet. Where was Ginger? "Come on, Fred. Help me find Ginger!" Fred didn't move. For more than 10 minutes Wendy looked for Ginger. Fred never moved.

(3) Then Wendy stopped and thought. "Thank you, Fred! You knew all along where Ginger was!" Wendy opened the closet door, and Ginger darted out.

Now, use the story to answer the questions on the following page.

1. The main character of this story is

   A. Rick   **C.** Fred
   B. Wendy   **D.** Ginger

2. Which word **best** describes the main character?

   A. helpful   **C.** caring
   B. mean   **D.** shy

3. Why doesn't Rick help take care of the cats?

   A. He is late for school.
   B. He likes to sleep later than Wendy.
   C. He takes care of the dog.
   D. He has allergies.

4. From the way Fred acts, you might think that he

   A. wants to be scratched again
   B. doesn't care where Ginger is
   C. likes Rick better than Wendy
   D. likes to wait for Wendy at the front door

In Your Own Words

5. Write a sentence to describe the main character in the story.

_____

_____

_____

_____

_____

Ask Yourself

1. Which character does the story mostly tell about?

4. Does it look to Wendy like Fred is helping her?

5. Who is the main character? What does she or he do or say?

Reading Literature

Read this story. Answer the questions that follow it.

Once a king had a garden. A bird that lived there sang the sweetest songs. "I must have that songbird for my own," said the king to his three sons. The eldest set out with a bow and arrow. The middle son set out with a slingshot and stones. The youngest set out with corn in a soft bag.

The eldest shot an arrow at the bird, but missed. The middle son shot three stones at the bird, but missed. "I tried," they both said and returned to the palace. The youngest son opened the bag with the sweet corn inside and left it in the garden. When the songbird swooped down to eat the corn, the son quickly but gently put the bird in the bag.

When the youngest son brought the bird to the king, it bird flew up to the rafters. Then she began to sing a sweet songs. The king ordered that the bird should be placed in a golden cage. "No, Father," said the youngest son. "A bird that sings this sweetly should not be in a cage."

"Your brothers may be lazy, but you have disobeyed! Leave the palace!" said the king.

---

1. The main characters in the story are

   A. the king and his three sons

   B. the king and the youngest son

   C. the king's three sons

   D. the king's eldest and youngest sons

2. Which words **best** describe the king?

   A. lazy and dull

   B. spoiled and easily angered

   C. kind and patient

   D. wise and considerate

Reading Literature

3. The way the older sons tried to capture the bird tells you that they

   A. love all animals except birds

   B. don't want to please their father

   C. are not very clever

   D. care about the bird

4. You can tell that the youngest son is kind because he

   A. kneels before his father the king

   B. tells his brothers not to shoot the bird

   C. captures the bird without hurting it

   D. leaves the palace

5. Which word does **not** describe the youngest son?

   A. clever

   B. brave

   C. smart

   D. unkind

6. Based on the actions and words of the three sons, which one would make the best future king?

   A. the middle son

   B. the eldest son

   C. the youngest son

   D. none of the above

Write It Out Think about the character traits of the youngest son. What do you think he will do next? Write one or two sentences explaining your answer.

7. _____

Reading Literature

Reading Literature

WORDS
TO KNOW   **Setting**   the time and place in which a story happens

---

Review It!   Read these sentences and figure out where and when the story takes place.

Mom said, "Turn out the light! You have to get up early tomorrow!" I turned off the lamp next to my bed and turned on my flashlight so I could read under the covers.

> **Hint**   The sentences "*Turn out the light! You have to get up early tomorrow!*" are clues to the time: night. The phrase *the lamp next to my bed* tells you the place: a bedroom.

Try It!   Read the passage from a story. As you read, underline the words or phrases that help you figure out the setting.

1. The twins Jack and Jake kissed their mother goodbye on the platform. A mixture
2. of sweat and tears poured down their faces. Record-breaking heat made it look like
3. everyone was crying. The boys climbed aboard with their father. He said this was the
4. start of a great adventure for them. The boys were not so sure. They were excited, but
5. they were also a bit scared. They'd never been away from home for more than one
6. night. Now for one week they wouldn't see their dog, their bedroom, or the park where
7. they rode their bikes. And they had never been so far away from home. Now they'd be
8. traveling over miles and miles of tracks to get to their grandmother's house. The boys
9. and their father found their seats. They looked out the window. The boys waved
10. good-bye to their mother.

Now, use the passage to answer the questions on the following page.

1. Where does this passage take place?

   A. in an airport   C. in a lake

   B. in a park   D. in a train station

Ask Yourself

2. What time of year does the passage **probably** take place?

   A. spring

   B. fall

   C. summer

   D. winter

1.

Which clues in lines 1, 3, 8, and 9 tell you where the story takes place?

3. Which of the following is part of the setting?

   A. Jack and Jake's dog

   B. a window

   C. the park near their home

   D. the twins' bedroom

2.

What words in line 2 help you figure out the when the story takes place?

4. Which of the following is part of the setting?

   A. a scary house

   B. record-high heat

   C. strong wind

   D. middle of the night

In Your Own Words

5. Write a title for the passage that would help the reader figure out the setting.

   _____

   _____

   _____

5.

What words in your title would help readers know the setting?

Reading Literature

On Your Own!

Read this story. Answer the questions that follow it.

Jane put down the book she was reading and took a sip of hot tea. She held onto the mug with both hands. Then she buttoned up a second sweater over the one she was already wearing. Jane wondered if she should put on another pair of socks.

She looked out the window. Storm clouds were rolling across the late afternoon sky. There would be no thunder or lightning. However, there would most certainly be at least another foot of snow, according to the car radio.

She and her dad had cut wood for the fireplace just two days earlier. Two feet of snow fell yesterday and knocked out power lines. The TV went blank. The stove didn't work. Mom had taken out the camping gear and was making soup in the fireplace. As she smelled the delicious soup, Jane began to wonder what the morning would bring. In an instant, she knew the answer—no school!

1. **Where does the story take place?**

   A. in the desert

   B. in a house

   C. in a school

   D. in a tent

2. **What time of year does the story take place?**

   A. winter

   B. fall

   C. summer

   D. spring

3.   Which is **not** part of the setting?

   A.   grocery store

   B.   window

   C.   rolling storm clouds

   D.   house

4.   The setting includes

   A.   a working TV

   B.   Jane's school

   C.   thunder and lightning

   D.   snow

5.   Read the sentence from the story.

   However there would most certainly be at least another foot of snow, according to the car radio.

   The sentence gives a clue that the story takes place

   A.   long ago

   B.   on the ocean

   C.   in modern times

   D.   in a kingdom

6.   What time of the day is it?

   A.   early morning

   B.   late afternoon

   C.   evening

   D.   late at night

Write It Out   How could the setting change in order for Jane to be reading outdoors?

7.   _____

   _____

   _____

   _____

   _____

   _____

   _____

Reading Literature

21 Theme

WORDS TO KNOW   **Theme**   the lesson or message the author wants the reader to learn

---

Review It!   Read these sentences. Use the Hint to figure out what lesson the author wants you to learn in the story.

Grasshopper played all summer long. He didn't store food for the winter as Ant did. When winter came, Grasshopper was hungry.

> **Hint**   What does Grasshopper do all summer? What about Ant? What happens in the winter helps you figure out the theme, or lesson, of the story: You have to prepare for hard times.

Try It!   Read the passage. As you read, <u>underline</u> the words or phrases that help you figure out the theme.

1. Henny and Penny sat on a tree branch talking. They had flown south each winter together many times. Now back north, they waited for their friends to join them. As they waited, they smoothed their dull, thin feathers. In the next tree, they saw a pretty newcomer. "Welcome!" said Henny.

2. "Hello! I'm Penny, and this is my friend Henny," said Penny. The pretty bird looked the two birds up and down and turned her back on them.

3. Just then, Henny and Penny's friends arrived. Instead of joining Henny and Penny on their branch, they crowded around the pretty bird. They admired her beautiful sleek feathers. The pretty bird began pecking at them. "Stay back! Don't touch my beautiful feathers!" she snapped.

Now, use the passage to answer the questions on the following page.

1. Based on paragraphs 1 and 2, which word **best** describes how Henny and Penny act?

   A. proud   C. welcoming

   B. indifferent   D. unfriendly

2. From the pretty bird's actions, you can tell she

   A. thinks she is better than Henny and Penny

   B. is busy playing with her own friends

   C. is too shy to say hello

   D. wishes she had friends like Henny and Penny

3. Which sentence **best** states the theme of this passage?

   A. You should not be friendly to newcomers.

   B. You should always be loyal to your friends.

   C. Friends in need are friends indeed.

   D. You should not be fooled by looks.

4. What is the message the author wants to give you?

   A. Birds of a feather should stick together.

   B. If you are beautiful, you can be unkind.

   C. Don't choose your friends by their looks.

   D. Friends in need are friends indeed.

In Your Own Words

5. What is the lesson Henny and Penny **probably** learn in the story?

   _____

   _____

   _____

   _____

Ask Yourself

1. Which words in paragraph 1 tell you about Henny and Penny?

2. Has anyone you know acted this way? If yes, how would you describe the person?

Reading Literature

5. How do Henny and Penny act toward the pretty bird? Why do they act this way?

Read this passage. Answer the questions that follow it.

"Let's ride!" said Sam as soon as Lee arrived. "Here!" he said. "Try these on. I bet they'll fit!" Sam said as held out a pair of cowboy boots.

They did fit. Now Lee was ready to ride. At least he was *dressed* to ride. But Lee had never been on a horse before. Sam had been riding nearly every day since his family moved out to the country last year. It was a big change from the city where the two boys grew up together, playing cowboys and riding the painted horses on the carousel in the park.

Sam was eager to show off his cowboy skills. Lee wanted to try a real horse. The friends walked to the corral. Sam helped Lee into the saddle. "Whoa!" said Lee with a nervous laugh. "This feels nothing like the carousel!" Sam mounted his own horse with ease.

Before long, Sam turned his horse back toward the corral. The horse Lee rode followed. "Why are we going back?" asked Lee, disappointed.

"Wind," said Sam. "Horses hate the wind. And the last thing I want is for my best friend to fall off a horse on his first day here!"

1. Sam and Lee are

   A. classmates
   B. brothers
   C. neighbors
   D. best friends

2. How does Sam feel about Lee's visit?

   A. excited
   B. annoyed
   C. nervous
   D. disappointed

3. How does Lee feel about riding?

   A. confident

   B. nervous

   C. angry

   D. indifferent

4. From Sam's actions, you can tell that he

   A. knows a lot about horses

   B. is sorry he moved away from Lee

   C. likes to show off his horses

   D. wants Lee to stay away from riding a horse

5. From what Lee says, you can tell that he

   A. wishes he were home in the city

   B. wants to pretend he is a cowboy

   C. would rather be on the carousel

   D. really wants to ride a horse

6. Which of the following **best** describes the theme of this passage?

   A. Friends stay friends no matter where they live.

   B. Friends share their clothes and shoes.

   C. Friends take good care of friends.

   D. Friends like to do the same kinds of things.

Write It Out   Use the passage to help you write a brief answer to the question below.

7. Suppose the boys had continued to ride in the wind, the horses got nervous, and Lee fell off the horse. How would the story's theme change?

_____

_____

_____

_____

_____

_____

Reading Literature

Reading Literature

WORDS TO KNOW	**Point of view** the perspective from which the narrator tells the story. Point of view tells you who the narrator is and how much he or she knows. Most narrators are either first-person or third-person narrators.

Review It!

Read these sentences. Use the Hint to figure out the point of view of the narrator in the story.

The rabbits wandered too far into the woods. Crouching behind the bushes, the wolf waited. As the rabbits came closer, he smiled and thought, "Hello, lunch!"

> **Hint**   The narrator knows what the wolf thinks. Think about what kind of narrator knows what characters think or feel.

Try It!

Read the passage. As you read, <u>underline</u> the words or phrases that help you figure out the point of view of the narrator.

1 Evan, Pat, and I met outside the movie theater. It was one of those huge theaters that
2 show a dozen movies. We had passes for the Blasts from the Past Movie Festival. There
3 were so many films to choose from! *Honey, I Shrunk the Kids* was on Screen 1. On
4 Screen 2, they were showing the first *King Kong*. On Screen 3, they were showing *The*
5 *Shaggy Dog,* a film about a dad who gets turned into a dog. The first *Star Wars* movie
6 was on Screen 3. I thought it would be hard to choose. Evan likes funny films. Pat loves
7 special effects. Me? I like everything! I said, "This one is so old the special effects will
8 probably be funny." My friends agreed. Can you guess which film we went to see?

Now, use the passages to answer the questions on the following page.

1. Who is the narrator in the passage?

    A. "I"   **C.** Evan

    B. Pat   **D.** Evan and Pat

2. In line 2, the pronoun *we* refers to

    A. Evan and Pat

    B. Evan and the narrator

    C. Evan, Pat, and another friend

    D. Evan, Pat, and the narrator

3. The point of view of the narrator in this story is

    A. first-person

    B. second-person

    C. first-person and third-person

    D. third-person

4. The reader learns the thoughts of

    A. Pat

    B. Evan

    C. the first-person narrator

    D. the third-person narrator

In Your Own Words

5. Rewrite the first sentence of the passage, changing the point of view.

_____

_____

_____

Ask Yourself

1.
Who is telling the story? What pronoun is used?

3.
Who is telling the story? Is the person telling the story a character in the story?

5.
What word in the sentence must you change in order to change the point of view?

Reading Literature

On Your Own! Read this story. Answer the questions that follow it.

Beth and her mother had spent two weeks traveling all over the country. They got up before dawn to fly in a helicopter. They rode a camel. They fed deer by hand. Beth thought, "I am so lucky my mother likes to travel!"

They arrived on the island, the next stop on their trip, in time for dinner. Her mother said, "It will be good to stay in one place for a couple of days." While her mother rested, Beth ran down to the beach to sign up for sailing lessons. A woman in a bathing suit was just locking the office door. "Not to worry," said the woman, smiling. "Hi, I'm the sailing teacher. I'll open up for you."

By the time Beth and her mother finished eating dinner, it was dark. The sky was filled with stars. On the walk back to their cabin, Beth's mother pointed up. "Look!" she cried, "A comet!"

"That's good luck, Mom," said Beth happily, "Maybe I'll have terrific weather for my first sailing lesson tomorrow!"

---

1. The point of view is

   A. first-person

   B. second-person

   C. third-person

   D. none of the above

2. Read this sentence from the story.

   They got up before dawn to fly in a helicopter.

   The pronoun *they* **refers to**

   A. Beth and her mother

   B. Beth and the sailing teacher

   C. Beth and the helicopter pilot

   D. Beth's mother and the helicopter pilot

3. Read this sentence from the story.

   Her mother said, "It will be good to stay in one place for a couple of days."

   In this sentence, the pronoun *her* refers to

   A. the sailing teacher

   B. Beth's mother

   C. Beth

   D. the narrator

4. Read these sentences from the story.

   Beth's mother pointed up. "Look!" she cried, "A comet!"

   In this sentence, the pronoun *she* refers to

   A. Beth's mother

   B. Beth

   C. the sailing teacher

   D. the narrator

5. Which is a correct statement about the story?

   A. The narrator is a character in the story.

   B. Beth's mother is not part of the story.

   C. The narrator is not part of the story.

   D. Beth, but not the sailing teacher, is a part of the story.

6. The narrator of the story knows

   A. what the characters do, and say only

   B. what the characters do, say, and think

   C. what only the main character does and says

   D. what some of the characters do and say

Write It Out Use the passage to write a brief answer to the question below.

7. Add a sentence to the end of the story, using the same point of view.

23 Author's Perspective

WORDS TO KNOW **Author's perspective**   what the author feels and thinks about a topic

 Review It!   Read these sentences. Use the Hint to figure out the author's perspective on the topic of pet dogs.

My parents got an adorable puppy as a wedding gift. A year later, I was born. I grew up with wonderful dogs and learned to take care of them. I believe every child should have a dog.

> **Hint**   What is the author trying to persuade you to do? Think about the words he uses such as *believe*, *adorable*, *wonderful*, and *every*.

 **Try It!**   Read the passage. As you read, <u>underline</u> the words or phrases that help you figure out the author's perspective.

① Yes, school uniforms can be boring. To wear the same thing every single day is no fun. Our uniform colors are gray, white, and navy. We can wear gray pants or a skirt and a white blouse or shirt. We can wear a blazer or a sweater, but it must be navy.

② However, school uniforms do make getting dressed in the morning easy. Once a month we don't have to wear the uniform. It's great to wear "real" clothes to school, but hard to put together the perfect outfit. Some kids show off the expensive clothes they have. I know that makes other kids feel bad. That's why I think school uniforms, although dull, are good. When we all wear the same thing, we spend more time thinking about learning.

Now, use the passage to answer the questions on the following page.

Reading Literature

1. The writer of the passage

   A. wears a uniform on Fridays

   B. wears only the blazer of a uniform

   C. does not wear a uniform to school

   D. wears a uniform to school

   1.
   What clues tell you that the author has personal experience with school uniforms?

2. Read this sentence from the passage.

   However, school uniforms do make getting dressed in the morning easy.

   This sentence shows that the writer sees that a school uniform

   A. can be a good thing   C. is sometimes boring

   B. is never a good thing   D. makes it difficult to get dressed

3. The author thinks that a bad thing about school uniforms is that they can be

   A. hard to put together   C. hard to find in the stores

   B. expensive   D. no fun to wear

4. Which of the following does **not** express the author's perspective on school uniforms?

   A. They are good because they help kids to think about school work.

   B. They are bad because kids can't show off their clothes.

   C. They are good because it is easy to get dressed in the morning.

   D. They can be dull because kids have to wear the same clothes every day.

   4.
   What does the author think and feel about wearing a uniform to school?

In Your Own Words

5. What is your perspective on school uniforms? Tell what you think and why.

   _____

   _____

   5.
   What words and phrases are you using to help explain your perspective?

Read this passage. Answer the questions that follow it.

Every neighborhood park should have a dog run. A dog run is a big playpen for dogs. Big dogs and small dogs all run and play together without having to be on leashes.

Most dog runs have water for dogs to drink. In the summer, some dog runs even have little wading pools. In a dog run, owners can easily clean up after their pets. That's good for dog owners as well as other people enjoying the park.

Dog runs are even good for people who don't have dogs. There are many reasons people don't have a dog. Some people are allergic to certain animals. Some buildings in the city don't allow dogs. At the dog run in my neighborhood, Mr. Fields sits on a bench inside the run every afternoon. He doesn't have a dog. He told me he's too old to take care of a pet dog. Here in the dog run he can enjoy other people's dogs. The dogs all seem to know him. They all run over to say hello to him. Mr. Fields pats the dogs. Sometimes he gives them small doggie treats.

1. **Read this sentence from the passage.**

   A dog run is a big playpen
   for dogs.

   From this sentence, you can tell the author feels that dog runs are for the neighborhood dogs like a

   A. children's playground
   B. ball field
   C. basketball court
   D. fountain

2. **One reason the author thinks some non-dog owners like dog runs is that**

   A. they are not allergic to dogs
   B. they are afraid of dogs
   C. they want to play with dogs but not clean up after them
   D. owners can easily clean up after their pets

Reading Literature

3. From this passage, you can tell that the author has

  A. talked to Mr. Fields in the market

  B. heard about the dog run from a neighbor

  C. been to the dog run himself

  D. filled a water bottle in the dog run

4. From the passage, you can tell that the author's perspective on dog runs is

  A. not positive

  B. very negative

  C. very positive

  D. not positive nor negative

5. According to the author,

  A. dog runs are only good for old men like Mr. Fields

  B. dog runs are good to have in all neighborhoods

  C. dog runs are needed only in the city

  D. dog runs are best for large parks but not small ones

6. Which of the following does the author **not** use to support his perspective?

  A. Dogs can run and play together without having to be on leashes.

  B. Dog owners can easily clean up after their pets.

  C. People who can't own dogs can enjoy them at the dog run.

  D. Dog runs cost little money to the city.

Write It Out   Use the passage to write a brief answer to the question below.

7. What is your perspective on dog runs? Explain your perspective.

Using Prior Knowledge to Make Predictions

WORDS TO KNOW

Prior knowledge what you already know before you read

Prediction a guess about what will happen, based on what you read and what you already know

---

Review It!

Read these sentences. Use the Hint to figure out what will happen next.

Maya rounded the bend. Her legs burned, her back ached, and her feet felt like lead. Keep going, Maya told herself. Just run! The finish line was just ahead.

Hint If you have ever run a race or watched one, the clues *run* and *finish line* can help you predict that Maya will finish the race and probably win it.

Try It!

Read the passage. As you read, <u>underline</u> things you already know that will help you make predictions.

(1) Sara looked down and was surprised to see that her hands were not shaking. "Breathe!"
(2) she said to herself. Sara closed her eyes. She counted to ten and slowly inhaled. She held
(3) the breath and pictured herself playing. In her mind, Sara saw herself seated on stage.
(4) She watched herself open the sheet music and adjust the bench to the right height.
(5) She saw her fingers glide across the keys. Then she let the air out, exhaling slowly and
(6) counting to twenty. Good. She felt calmer. Sara opened her eyes. She was ready. Then
(7) she heard, "The next piece will be played by Sara Blanton." Sara smiled and walked out
(8) on stage.

Now, use the passages to answer the questions on the following page.

Reading Literature

1. What might you have experienced or seen on TV that would help you make a prediction about this passage?

   A. playing the violin   **C.** being an actor

   B. performing   **D.** listening to music

Ask Yourself

2. Read this sentence from the passage.

   > Sara looked down and was surprised to see that her hands were not shaking.

   The word that **best** describes how Sara feels is

   A. happy   **C.** excited

   B. lonely   **D.** nervous

   2. Have you ever given a performance in front of an audience? How did you feel?

3. Based on what you already know, why does Sara **probably** take long, slow breaths?

   A. It calms her nerves.   **C.** She likes to use her imagination.

   B. She enjoys doing yoga.   **D.** It helps her asthma.

4. What will Sara **most likely** do next?

   A. play the piano   **C.** sing a song

   B. not go out on stage   **D.** do a dance

   4. What clues do you read in the passage that help you make a prediction about what Sara will do next?

In Your Own Words

5. Make a prediction about what kind of performance Sara will give. Use what you know already and what you read in the passage.

   _____

   _____

   _____

   _____

   _____

   5. What does Sara do to get ready? How does she feel just before she walks out on stage?

Reading Literature

On Your Own! Read this passage. Answer the questions that follow it.

Jason got up and started getting ready for school. His big sister, Julie, didn't say anything. "Have a happy day at school, kids," his mother said as she left for work.

"Happy *day*?" thought Jason, "Just a happy *day*? Isn't she forgetting something?"

"Jason, please return this library book on your way home," Dad said. Where were the cards, the presents?

At school Jason's teacher, Mr. Evans, didn't say anything. His friends didn't say anything. It was just an ordinary day at school!

After school, Jason went to the library to return Dad's book. On his way home, he couldn't help thinking about how no one remembered. When he opened the front door, everything was quiet and dark. "I guess no one's even home," he thought. Suddenly the whole house lit up. Camera flashes went off and Jason's whole family and all his friends jumped out yelled, "Surprise!" Even Mr. Evans was there!

Jason's mother carried in a huge cake with candles, and everyone sang. Dad brought out wrapped gifts.

---

1. Your prior knowledge helps you predict that this story is going to be about

   A. Jason's teacher's birthday

   B. Jason's birthday

   C. Jason's special day in school

   D. Jason's sister's birthday

2. Read this sentence from the passage.

   "Just a happy day?"

   What day is Jason thinking of?

   A. Thanksgiving

   B. the next day

   C. his birthday

   D. Easter

3. Based on your past experience, how does Jason **probably** feel before going to school?

   A. happy

   B. disappointed

   C. amused

   D. jealous

4. Using your prior knowledge, how do you think Jason will feel at the end of the day?

   A. relieved

   B. happy

   C. angry

   D. sad

5. Which of the following will Jason **not** do next?

   A. blow out the candles

   B. read the cards

   C. fall asleep

   D. open the presents

6. Based on what you already know, you can predict that Jason's friends will

   A. go to school

   B. go to the mall

   C. do homework

   D. share the cake

Write It Out Use the passage to help you write a brief answer to the question below.

7. What do you predict Jason will say to his friends and family at the end of the story?

_____

_____

_____

_____

_____

_____

LESSON 25 — Types of Sentences

WORDS TO KNOW

Simple sentence a group words that has a subject and a predicate. **Sentence fragment** a group of words that lacks a subject or a predicate. **Compound sentence** a combination of two sentences that are independent from each other. **Appositive phrase** a phrase used to describe a subject. **Participial phrase** a phrase that describes a predicate.

 Read these sentences. Use the Hint to identify the different kinds of sentences the writer uses.

Dripping wet, Josh hoisted himself out of the pool. Tess, the assistant coach, stopped the timer, and she smiled. "You did it!" she said. "A new record!"

> **Hint** Which sentence has a subject and predicate? Do you see a sentence that has two sentences put together? Think about which sentences contain phrases that describe nouns.

 Read the passage. As you read, use different marks to identify different kinds of sentences.

① Amy, my little sister, loves animals. One day Amy took a slice of bread, and she headed
② outside. Just then, Mom walked into the kitchen. "Hungry?" she asked Amy. "Would
③ you like some butter on that? A bit of jam?"

④ "No," said Amy. She went out. From the window my twin sister, Ann, Mom, and I
⑤ watched. Bending down, Amy stared at the seam between two slabs of concrete. Then
⑥ she tore off bits of bread, but she didn't put any of them in her mouth.

⑦ When Amy walked in the door, Mom asked, "Who ate the bread?"

⑧ Amy said, "The ants."

Now, use the passages to answer the questions on the following page.

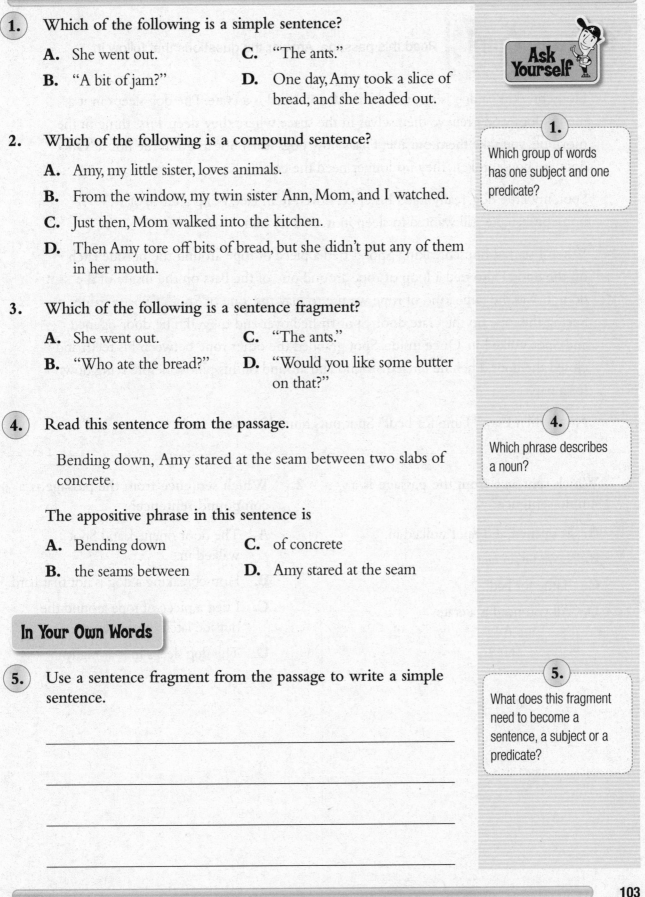

1. Which of the following is a simple sentence?

   A. She went out.

   B. "A bit of jam?"

   C. "The ants."

   D. One day, Amy took a slice of bread, and she headed out.

Ask Yourself

1.
Which group of words has one subject and one predicate?

2. Which of the following is a compound sentence?

   A. Amy, my little sister, loves animals.

   B. From the window, my twin sister Ann, Mom, and I watched.

   C. Just then, Mom walked into the kitchen.

   D. Then Amy tore off bits of bread, but she didn't put any of them in her mouth.

3. Which of the following is a sentence fragment?

   A. She went out.

   B. "Who ate the bread?"

   C. "The ants."

   D. "Would you like some butter on that?"

4. Read this sentence from the passage.

   Bending down, Amy stared at the seam between two slabs of concrete.

   The appositive phrase in this sentence is

   A. Bending down

   B. the seams between

   C. of concrete

   D. Amy stared at the seam

4.
Which phrase describes a noun?

In Your Own Words

5. Use a sentence fragment from the passage to write a simple sentence.

   _____

   _____

   _____

5.
What does this fragment need to become a sentence, a subject or a predicate?

Housebreaking a dog is not that hard. All you need is a crate. The dog sleeps in it at night. Dogs won't relieve themselves in the space where they sleep. First thing in the morning, you take them outside. That's how dogs learn not to go in the house. Once dogs are housebroken, they no longer need the crate.

Spot, my little dog, really liked his crate. Loved it, in fact. Long after Spot was housebroken, he still wanted to sleep in it. So I let him.

When I started housebreaking Spot, I tied a piece of rope around the outside latch on the door. I also tied a loop of rope around one of the bars on the inside of the door. It was the same kind of rope we use to play tug, one of Spot's favorite games. Seeing the rope on the crate door, Spot rushed over and tugged. The door opened, and Spot walked in. Once inside, Spot grabbed the other rope between his teeth and closed the door. Then he circled around and around on his pillow before lying down for a nap.

Now when I say, "Time for bed!" Spot puts himself to bed!

1. Which sentence from the passage is a simple sentence?

   A. It opened, and Spot walked in.

   B. Loved it, in fact.

   C. Time for bed!

   D. All you need is a crate.

2. Which sentence from the passage is a compound sentence?

   A. The door opened, and Spot walked in.

   B. Housebreaking a dog is not that hard.

   C. I tied a piece of rope around the outside latch on the door.

   D. The dog sleeps in it at night.

3. A group of words that is a sentence fragment is

A. The dog sleeps in it at night

B. So I let him.

C. Loved it, in fact.

D. Spot puts himself to bed!

4. Read this sentence from the passage.

Spot, my little dog, really liked his crate.

Which group of words is an appositive phrase?

A. Spot

B. my little dog

C. really liked

D. liked his crate

5. Which sentence from the passage has an appositive phrase?

A. It was the same kind of rope we use to play tug, one of Spot's favorite games.

B. I also tied a loop of rope around one of the bars on the inside of the door.

C. Housebreaking a dog is not that hard.

D. That's how dogs learn not to go in the house.

6. Which sentence from the passage has a participial phrase?

A. When I started housebreaking Spot, I tied a piece of rope around the outside latch on the door.

B. The door opened, and Spot walked in.

C. Then he circled around and around on his pillow before lying down for a nap.

D. Seeing the rope on the crate door, Spot rushed over and tugged.

Write It Out Use the passage to help you write a brief answer to the question below.

7. Choose a compound sentence in the passage. Write it as two simple sentences.

_____

_____

_____

_____

_____

WORDS TO KNOW

Punctuation   marks in printed text that help make reading easier
End marks   marks such as a period, question mark, or exclamation point that show where sentences end and signal different kinds of sentences
Comma   mark that appears between the day and year, between the names of regions in a location, and between items in a series

 **Read these sentences. Use the Hint to figure out where the missing commas belong.**

Ed was born on March 7 1998. For his birthday dinner, Ed wants salad made with carrots tomatoes and onions that were grown locally in Springfield Indiana.

> **Hint**   The day and year need to be separated with a comma: *March 7, 1998.* The three vegetables also need to be separated with commas: *carrots, tomatoes, and onions.* Use a comma to separate city and state: *Springfield, Indiana.*

 Read the passage. As you read, look for places with missing punctuation and make a mark. Circle incorrect punctuation.

(1) What might school vacations 100 years from now be like They could be a lot longer
(2) than they are today. Imagine it is December 20 2110. A family that just left to visit
(3) cousins on the Moon might leave this message on their answering machine.

(4) "You have reached the Suarez family's answering machine We are spending the holiday
(5) on Lunar Lake Moontown. If you would like to leave a message for Joe, please press 3
(6) now. Press 4 for Jay press 6 for Jim and press 8 for Jan. We'll return on February, 2 2111.
(7) Happy New Year!"

Now, use the passage to answer the questions on the following page.

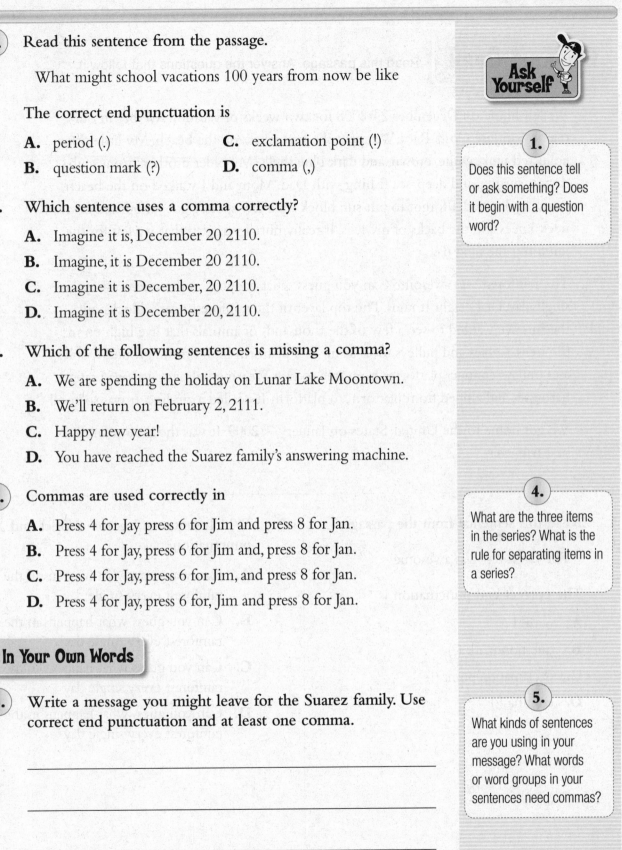

1. Read this sentence from the passage.

What might school vacations 100 years from now be like

The correct end punctuation is

A. period (.)   **C.** exclamation point (!)

B. question mark (?)   **D.** comma (,)

2. Which sentence uses a comma correctly?

A. Imagine it is, December 20 2110.

B. Imagine, it is December 20 2110.

C. Imagine it is December, 20 2110.

D. Imagine it is December 20, 2110.

3. Which of the following sentences is missing a comma?

A. We are spending the holiday on Lunar Lake Moontown.

B. We'll return on February 2, 2111.

C. Happy new year!

D. You have reached the Suarez family's answering machine.

4. Commas are used correctly in

A. Press 4 for Jay press 6 for Jim and press 8 for Jan.

B. Press 4 for Jay, press 6 for Jim and, press 8 for Jan.

C. Press 4 for Jay, press 6 for Jim, and press 8 for Jan.

D. Press 4 for Jay, press 6 for, Jim and press 8 for Jan.

In Your Own Words

5. Write a message you might leave for the Suarez family. Use correct end punctuation and at least one comma.

_____

_____

_____

_____

Ask Yourself

1.
Does this sentence tell or ask something? Does it begin with a question word?

4.
What are the three items in the series? What is the rule for separating items in a series?

5.
What kinds of sentences are you using in your message? What words or word groups in your sentences need commas?

Writing and Editing

We left home on December 24 2008 for two weeks of vacation. We began our trip in San Jose Costa Rica. We spent the first week, on the beach. My little sister collected pink, white, brown, and dark blue shells. My older brothers went scuba diving, surfing, and deep-sea fishing with Dad. Mom and I walked on the beach, swam, and surfed. I forgot to put sun block on a few spots. I got sunburned on my neck knees and the backs of my legs. It really hurt I was glad that we left for the rainforest the next day.

The rainforest was awesome Can you guess what happens in the rainforest every single day That's right It rains. The top layer of the rainforest nearly blocks out the sun. We wanted to see a few of the thousands of animals that live high up in the trees. Cables and pulleys took us up to a platform high off the ground. Cables, and pulleys connect platforms from tree to tree. Wearing helmets, we sat in safety harnesses and zipped from platform to platform It's called a zip line. It was so cool!

We got home to the United, States on January 7, 2009. It was the Simon family's best trip ever

---

1. Read this sentence from the passage.

    The rainforest was awesome

    The correct end punctuation is

    A. period (.)

    B. question mark (?)

    C. exclamation point (!)

    D. comma (,)

2. **Which sentence has the correct end punctuation?**

    A. Can you guess what happens in the rainforest every single day?

    B. Can you guess what happens in the rainforest every single day!

    C. Can you guess what happens in the rainforest every single day.

    D. Can you guess what happens in the rainforest every single day,

3. Read this sentence from the passage.

> We left home on December
> 24 2009 for two weeks of vacation.

The sentence needs a comma

A. after *December*

B. before *December*

C. after *24*

D. after *weeks*

4. Which sentence uses the comma correctly?

A. Cables, and pulleys connect platforms from tree to tree.

B. We spent the first week, on the beach.

C. We got home to the United, States on January 7, 2010.

D. We began our trip in San Jose, Costa Rica.

5. Which sentence has a comma in the **wrong** place?

A. The top layer of the rainforest nearly blocks out the sun.

B. My little sister collected pink, white, brown, and dark blue shells.

C. My older brothers went scuba diving, surfing, and deep-sea fishing.

D. I got sunburned on my neck, knees, and the backs, of my legs.

6. Which sentence uses end punctuation and commas correctly?

A. It was the Simon family's best trip, ever?

B. Mom and I walked on the beach, swam, and surfed.

C. I got sunburned on my neck, knees and the backs of my legs

D. Can you guess what happens, in the rainforest every single day!

Write It Out Use the passage to help you write a brief answer to the question below.

7. What three activities would you like to do with the Simon family on their vacation? Use correct punctuation in your sentences.

_____

_____

_____

_____

_____

LESSON 27 — Capitalization

WORDS TO KNOW   **Capitalization**   uppercase letters used for important words

Review It!   Read these sentences. Use the Hint to figure out which words should be capitalized.

my mother had to go to dr. park's office.
I went with her because i wanted to
get some books from the library right
next door.

> **Hint**   Think about the rules for capitalization. Which words in the sentences do not follow these rules? Are the proper nouns capitalized? Is the personal pronoun capitalized?

Try It!   Read the passage. <u>Circle</u> the letters that should be capitalized.

1. on my way to school one morning, i saw that Poppa's perfect pizza was dark. That
2. was odd, i thought. I like to think about mr. poppa tossing and stretching the dough
3. to make a perfect pizza for my after-school snack. Right next door, i saw that tap
4. with tina, the dance school my sister goes to, was also dark. The City was changing
5. so quickly. I remembered the meeting my mother went to last night at the town hall.
6. People wanted to know how they could help protect small stores in the neighborhood.
7. big developers were buying up whole city blocks and raising rents so high that small
8. store owners had to shut down their stores. my Sister will be so upset when she hears
9. about tap with tina. I'll talk to ms. maribelle, my teacher. I'm sure she will know what
10. kids can do to help.

Now, use the passage to answer the questions on the following page.

1. Read this sentence from the passage.

   on my way to school one morning, i saw that Poppa's perfect pizza was dark.

   The words that should be capitalized are

   A. on, school, i, pizza,
   B. i, that, perfect, pizza
   C. school, i, perfect, pizza
   D. on, i, perfect, pizza

1.

What words are proper nouns? Do you see the pronoun *I*?

2. Which sentence uses capital letters correctly?

   A. my Sister will be so upset.
   B. My Sister will be so upset.
   C. My sister will be so upset.
   D. My Sister will be SO upset.

3. Capital letters are correctly used in which of the following phrases?

   A. Poppa's Perfect pizza
   B. tap with Tina
   C. Tap with Tina
   D. Ms. maribelle

4. Which of the following sentences is missing **one** capital letter?

   A. I'll talk to ms. Maribelle, my teacher.
   B. The City is changing so quickly.
   C. I remembered the meeting my mother went to last night at the town hall.
   D. My Sister will be so upset when she hears about tap with tina.

4.

What is the capitalization rule about the title before a person's name?

In Your Own Words

5. Suppose you are the narrator. Write a note to your teacher asking about how you could help the pizza shop and dance school to stay open.

   _____

   _____

   _____

5.

What proper nouns will you use in your note? Which letters should be capitalized?

Writing and Editing

Read this passage. Answer the questions that follow it.

Sue wandered around the library. she didn't need a book because she borrowed three just yesterday. today she was meeting her little cousin janet at the library to help her with her homework.

"Hi," whispered janet, remembering to speak softly in the library. "sorry i am late. My teacher was reading to us, and we wanted him to finish the chapter."

Sue smiled. mr. Vans had been Sue's teacher, too. he sure did love to read. He made *her* want to read. All it took was one book. That's all any kid needs to find out how much fun reading can be. for sue, that one special book was about a doctor. This doctor used to treat people, but people stopped going to see him. they thought He was odd. His house was filled with animals, and he talked to them. sue loved dr. doolittle! That one book led her to all the other dr. doolittle adventures written by hugh lofting.

Janet tugged on Sue's sleeve. "can we get started with my homework now? I just started dr. Doolittle goes to the moon, and i want to find out what happens next!"

---

1. Read this sentence from the passage.

   today she was meeting her little cousin janet at the library to help her with her homework.

   The words that should start with a capital letter are

   A. today, cousin

   B. cousin, janet

   C. today, janet

   D. she, library

2. Which sentence uses capital letters correctly?

   A. sorry i am late.

   B. Sorry I am late.

   C. sorry I am late.

   D. Sorry I am Late.

3. Which sentence uses capital letters correctly?

   A. "hi," whispered Janet, remembering to speak softly in the library.

   B. "Hi," whispered Janet, remembering to speak softly in the library.

   C. "hi," whispered janet, remembering to speak softly in the library.

   D. "Hi," whispered janet, remembering to speak softly in the library.

4. Which book title is correctly capitalized?

   A. Dr. Doolittle Goes to the Moon

   B. dr. Doolittle Goes to the Moon

   C. Dr. doolittle goes to the Moon

   D. dr. Doolittle Goes to the moon

5. Which of the following sentences is missing **one** capital letter?

   A. sue loved dr. doolittle!

   B. mr. Vans had been sue's teacher, too.

   C. he sure did love to read.

   D. He made her want to read.

6. Which sentence uses capital letters correctly?

   A. The dr. Doolittle adventures were written by Hugh Lofting.

   B. The Dr. doolittle adventures were written by hugh Lofting.

   C. The Dr. Doolittle Adventures were written by Hugh lofting.

   D. The Dr. Doolittle adventures were written by Hugh Lofting.

Write It Out Use the passage to help you write a brief answer to the question below.

7. What is your favorite storybook? Write a few sentences that include the title, the author's name, and a short summary of the story's plot. Use capital letters correctly in your answer.

   _____

   _____

   _____

Writing and Editing

LESSON
28 > Spelling

WORDS TO KNOW

Spelling patterns of letters in English words. It helps you to sound out words carefully and to remember some general rules to follow: For example, use *i* before *e* except after *c*; for words ending in *y* with two or more syllables, change the *y* to *i* before adding a suffix.

Review It!

Read these sentences. Use the Hint to figure out how to spell the underlined words correctly.

Lane pointed to the <u>read</u>-headed kids on the swings. She had never seen them before. So she <u>askd</u> Jose if they were his <u>freinds</u>.

> **Hint** Which spelling rule can you use for each underlined word? The correct spellings are *red*, *asked*, and *friends*. The words *read* and *red* sound the same, so you need to figure out which spelling makes sense in the sentence.

Try It!

Read the passage. As you read, circle the words that are misspelled.

1. The morning after the snoustorm was so beautyful! Tara felt lucky becawse school
2. wus closed! Tara helped her too-year-old brother, Bobby, into his knew snowsuit. She
3. tyed his hood under his chin, laced up his boots, and helped him put on his mittens.
4. Then she put on her own parka, hat, scarf, and gluves. Tara checkt her watch. It was
5. getting late. They hurryed to the park at the end of the block. When they got their,
6. Bobby sat down in the snow. Tara sat down next to him. "Let's make snow angels!" she
7. said waveing her arms and legs. But Bobby did'nt move. Tara sat up and looked at her
8. little brother. He was fast asleep! "Geting dressed for winter sure is tiring!" Tara pickd
9. Bobby up and carried him home.

Now, use the passage to answer the questions on the following page.

Writing and Editing

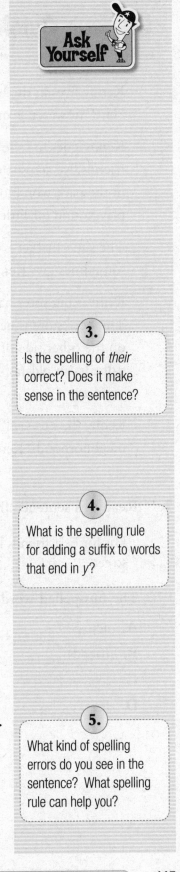

1. Read this sentence from the passage.

   Tara felt lucky becawse school was closed.

   The misspelled word is

   A. felt   **C.** closed

   B. becawse   **D.** was

2. **Which sentence has a spelling error?**

   A. Tara checkt her watch.

   B. It was getting late.

   C. Tara sat down next to him.

   D. "Let's make snow angels!"

3. Read this sentence from the passage.

   When they got <u>their</u>, Bobby sat down in the snow.

   The correct spelling of the underlined word is

   A. they're   **C.** there

   B. thare   **D.** thier

   Ask Yourself 3.
   Is the spelling of *their* correct? Does it make sense in the sentence?

4. **Which sentence does not have a spelling error?**

   A. She tyed his hood under his chin and laced up his boots.

   B. They hurryed to the park at the end of the block.

   C. The morning after the snowstorm was so beautyful!

   D. Tara sat up and looked at her little brother.

   Ask Yourself 4.
   What is the spelling rule for adding a suffix to words that end in *y*?

In Your Own Words

5. Rewrite the first sentence of the passage using correct spelling.

   _____

   _____

   _____

   Ask Yourself 5.
   What kind of spelling errors do you see in the sentence? What spelling rule can help you?

Writing and Editing

Read this passage. Answer the questions that follow it.

Kenny lives in the big city. There are huge skyscrapers in every direction. Kenny's "city," however, is quite small. His hole world can be found on just two city blocks.

Kenny goes to school around the corner from his apartment building. His for best friends live across the street. Happily, the buddys are in the same class. They play ball in the park won block west. The park has a brand-new baseball feild. Their's a new playground for little kids, too.

The supermarket is one block east. Kenny nose the manager, Mr. Green. Mr. Green sometimes givs Kenny odd jobs to do around the store.

Kenny's big sister hangs out at the bookstore. It is two blocks north of there building. The bookstore is next door to a movie theater. His mother likes the coffee shop on the other side of the theater. Two doors from the coffee shop is Kenny's favorite store. Its an old-fashioned toy store. The coolest wind-up toies sit in the display window.

Kenny likes to say, "Its a big city, but everything I need is write here in my nieghborhood." Kenny wouldn't want to live anywhere else.

---

1. Read this sentence from the passage.

   His for best friends live across the street.

   The misspelled word is

   A. across
   B. friends
   C. live
   D. for

2. Read this sentence from the passage.

   They play ball in the park <u>won</u> block west.

   The correct spelling of the underlined word is

   A. on
   B. wun
   C. one
   D. wan

3. **Which sentence has a spelling error?**

   A. Kenny's "city," however, is quite small.

   B. The bookstore is next door to a movie theater.

   C. It is two blocks north of there building.

   D. Kenny's big sister hangs out at the bookstore.

4. **Which sentence has a spelling error?**

   A. Kenny goes to school around the corner from his apartment building.

   B. The coolest wind-up toies sit in the window.

   C. Two doors from the coffee shop is Kenny's favorite store.

   D. His mother likes the coffee shop on the other side of the theater.

5. **Which sentence does not have a spelling error?**

   A. Kenny wouldn't want to live anywhere else.

   B. Kenny nose the manager, Mr. Green.

   C. The park has a brand new baseball feild.

   D. His hole world can be found on just two city blocks.

6. **Which sentence has two spelling errors?**

   A. Its an old-fashioned toy store.

   B. Their's a new playground for little kids, two.

   C. Kenny likes to say, "Its a big city."

   D. Happily, the buddys are in the same class.

Write It Out Use the passage to help you write a brief answer to the question below.

7. **What is your neighborhood like? Write 2–3 sentences to tell what you like about it. Check your sentences to see if you have spelled your words correctly.**

   _____

   _____

   _____

   _____

   _____

   _____

LESSON 29 — Subject-Verb Agreement

WORDS TO KNOW   **Subject-verb agreement**   using the right verb with the subject of a sentence. Look to see if the subject is singular or plural to decide which verb to use.

Read these sentences. Use the Hint to determine if the subject and the verb agree in each sentence.

The Santos twins go to the same school. After school, Luis plays soccer. Rico takes his guitar lesson.

> **Hint**   Notice that the first sentence has a plural subject so the verb *go* is correct. The second and third sentences have singular subjects and verbs that agree with them.

Read the passage. As you read, <u>circle</u> the subjects. <u>Underline</u> the verbs. If the subject and verb do not agree, <u>draw a box</u> around the verb.

(1) On the first Monday of each semester, Mr. Wilson posts the list of after-school
(2) clubs. He also send the list by e-mail. All the kids looks for their favorite teachers
(3) or activities. The art teacher, Ms. Mindy, are new. The list say she will teach a class
(4) in watercolors on Mondays. Mr. Lee has a cooking club on Tuesdays. The list also
(5) says that the soccer team meets on Tuesdays and Thursdays. The library is open for
(6) homework help every day until 5:30 P.M.

(7) Miranda plans to join the Homework Helpers club. She like to read to the little kids.
(8) Sam sing beautifully. He is always the first to sign up for the glee club. Jen and Ken is
(9) excited about the new dance club. They wants to learn to cha-cha-cha.

Now, use the passage to answer the questions on the following page.

Writing and Editing

118

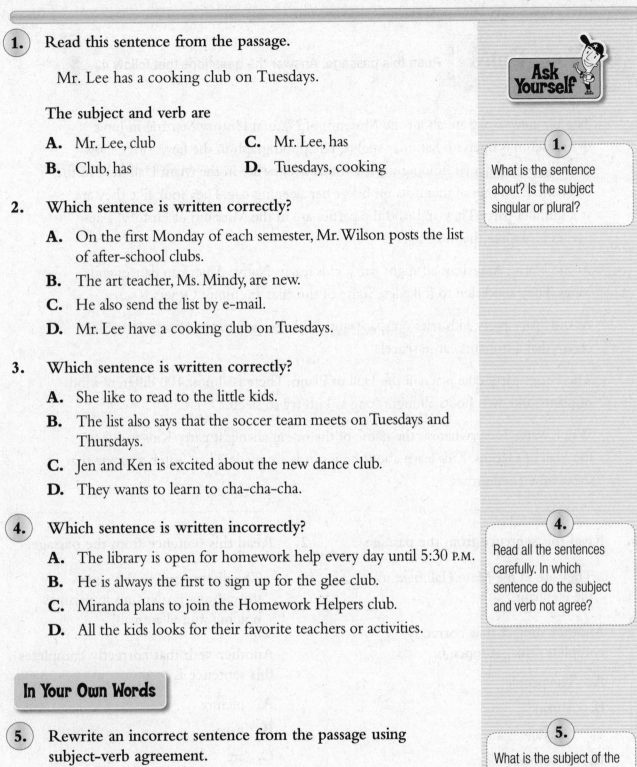

1. Read this sentence from the passage.

Mr. Lee has a cooking club on Tuesdays.

The subject and verb are

A. Mr. Lee, club   C. Mr. Lee, has

B. Club, has   D. Tuesdays, cooking

1.
What is the sentence about? Is the subject singular or plural?

2. Which sentence is written correctly?

A. On the first Monday of each semester, Mr. Wilson posts the list of after-school clubs.

B. The art teacher, Ms. Mindy, are new.

C. He also send the list by e-mail.

D. Mr. Lee have a cooking club on Tuesdays.

3. Which sentence is written correctly?

A. She like to read to the little kids.

B. The list also says that the soccer team meets on Tuesdays and Thursdays.

C. Jen and Ken is excited about the new dance club.

D. They wants to learn to cha-cha-cha.

4. Which sentence is written incorrectly?

A. The library is open for homework help every day until 5:30 P.M.

B. He is always the first to sign up for the glee club.

C. Miranda plans to join the Homework Helpers club.

D. All the kids looks for their favorite teachers or activities.

4.
Read all the sentences carefully. In which sentence do the subject and verb not agree?

In Your Own Words

5. Rewrite an incorrect sentence from the passage using subject-verb agreement.

_____

_____

_____

5.
What is the subject of the sentence? What is the correct verb form to use?

Writing and Editing

The big news story are about the Museum of Natural History. Starting in June, the museum is open on Saturday nights. The photograph in the news story show grown-ups in pajamas holding stuffed animals! They are in the Main Hall next to the elephant. Each one of them sits on his or her sleeping bag. They look like they are at a slumber party. They are! And the parties are in the Museum of History! These parties looks like the most fun.

At the Native American all-night party, kids learns Native American dances and songs. They also listen to folktales. Some of the tales are funny. Others is scary.

At the Space party, kids tries on space suits. Kid also gets to taste freeze-dried ice cream that astronauts eat in space!

The Forest party take place in the Hall of Plants. There is almost 100 different kinds of plants, and owls hoots all night long as kids try to sleep.

Water, Water, Everywhere is the name of the ocean all-night party. Kids meets in the Hall of Oceans. Kids learn about how pearls are made. They watch a movie that show how coral grows.

---

1. Read this sentence from the passage.

They are in the Main Hall next to the elephant.

Another subject that correctly completes this sentence is

A. The people

B. A man

C. An adult

D. A woman

2. Read this sentence from the passage.

The photograph in the news story shows grown-ups in pajamas holding stuffed animals!

Another verb that correctly completes this sentence is

A. picture

B. have

C. are

D. has

3. Which sentence is written correctly?

   A. Kid also gets to taste freeze-dried ice cream that astronauts eat in space.

   B. Kids meets in the Hall of Oceans.

   C. At the Native American all-night party, kids learn Native American dances and songs.

   D. They watch a movie that show how coral grows.

4. Which sentence is written correctly?

   A. The big news story are about the Museum of Natural History.

   B. Starting in June, the museum is open on Saturday nights.

   C. Kids meets in the Hall of Oceans.

   D. At the Space party, kids tries on space suits.

5. The sentence that is written incorrectly is

   A. They also listen to folktales.

   B. Some of the tales are funny.

   C. Others is scary.

   D. Kids learn dances and songs.

6. Which sentence is written correctly?

   A. These parties looks like the most fun.

   B. The Forest party takes place in the Hall of Plants.

   C. There is almost 100 different kinds of plants, and owls hoots all night long as kids try to sleep.

   D. At the Space party, kids tries on space suits.

Write It Out   Use the passage to help you write a brief answer to the question below.

7. Which party at the Museum of Natural History sounds most interesting to you? Explain. Use correct subject-verb agreement in your answer.

_____

_____

_____

_____

_____

Writing and Editing

Words to Know

appositive phrase   phrase that describes a subject   **(Page 102)**

author's perspective   what the author feels and thinks about a topic   **(Page 94)**

author's purpose   the reason or reasons an author has for writing. Authors often write to entertain, teach, or tell something, or to affect how a reader feels about something.   **(Page 70)**

C   **capitalization**   uppercase letters used for important words   **(Page 110)**

cause and effect   A **cause** is the reason something happens and the **effect** is the result of a cause.   **(Page 58)**

characters   the main people or animals in a story. Characters have traits that make them act and speak in certain ways.   **(Page 78)**

comma   a mark that appears between the day and year, between the names of regions in a location, and between items in a series   **(Page 106)**

compare and contrast   show how things are alike and different   **(Page 62)**

compound sentence   two simple sentences put together   **(Page 102)**

conclusions   ideas you get from clues in the passage, your own prior knowledge, and common sense   **(Page 42)**

C   **context clues**   words, phrases, or sentences around or near an unfamiliar word that help you understand its meaning   **(Page 22)**

E   **end marks**   marks such as a period, question mark, or exclamation point that show where sentences end and signal different kinds of sentences   **(Page 106)**

F   **fact**   a statement that is true and can be proven. An **opinion** is a statement that gives someone's feelings or beliefs about a topic. An opinion cannot be proven.   **(Page 46)**

G   **genres**   different types of literature. The main genres are fiction, poetry, drama, and nonfiction. Fiction includes different kinds of made-up stories, such as fairy tales. Poetry has short lines and is written in stanzas. Sometimes it rhymes. Drama uses dialogue and stage directions.   **(Page 66)**

graphic organizers   illustrations that make ideas clear with lines and shapes. Graphic organizers include webs and diagrams.   **(Page 18)**

graphics visual aids that provide information in a clear, short form. Charts, tables, and bar graphs are examples of graphics. Bar graphs use bars instead of words to compare information. **(Page 14)**

 heading a word or phrase at the top of a paragraph that tells what the paragraph is about **(Page 6)**

 inferences educated guesses based on what you're reading and what you already know. When you make an inference, you're figuring out something which the writer has not told you directly. **(Page 38)**

M **main idea** what most of the sentences in a passage or story are about. It is also the most important point that the author makes about a subject. **(Page 30)**

P **participial phrase** a phrase that describes a predicate **(Page 102)**

plot what happens in a story. A plot includes a problem or conflict that the main character or characters try to solve. **(Page 74)**

 point of view the perspective from which the narrator tells the story. Point of view tells you who the narrator is and how much he or she knows. Most narrators are either first-person or third-person narrators. **(Page 90)**

prediction a guess about what will happen, based on what you read and what you already know **(Page 98)**

prior knowledge what you already know before you read **(Page 98)**

punctuation marks in printed text that help make reading easier **(Page 106)**

Q **questions** can help you better understand what you're reading. Try questions beginning with *who, what, when, where, why* and *how* first. **(Page 26)**

R **reference sources** books and periodicals, such as newspapers and magazines, that provide facts and information. Parts within reference sources, such as indexes and tables of contents, make finding information easier. **(Page 10)**

S **sentence fragment** a group of words that lacks a subject or a predicate **(Page 102)**

sequence the order in which events take place. Sequence is also called time order or chronological order. **(Page 54)**

S   **setting**   the time and place in which a story happens   **(Page 82)**

simple sentence   a group of words that has a subject and a predicate   **(Page 102)**

spelling   patterns of letters in English words. It helps you to sound out words carefully and to remember some general rules to follow: For example, use *i* before *e* except after *c*; for words ending in *y* with two or more syllables, change the *y* to *i* before adding a suffix.   **(Page 114)**

subject-verb agreement   using the right verb with the subject of a sentence. Look to see if the subject is singular or plural to decide which verb to use—*A bird sings. Many birds sing*.   **(Page 118)**

summarizing   giving the main idea and important details of the text in your own words   **(Page 50)**

supporting details   pieces of information that tell about the main idea   **(Page 34)**

T   **theme**   the lesson or message the author wants the reader to learn   **(Page 86)**

My Words

125